C000240782

The CAMRA Guide to
Cellarmanship

by Ivor Clissold

Author: Ivor Clissold

Published by CAMRA Books, Campaign for Real Ale, 230 Hatfield Road, St Albans AL1 4LW
Tel: 01727 867201 Fax: 01727 867670
Managing Editor: Mark Webb

ISBN 1-85249-126-4

First Edition, January 1997

Great effort has gone into researching the contents of this book, but no responsibility can be taken for errors.

CONTENTS

To Margaret, Alex and Jim: their forbearance allowed me 20 years of research.

Illustrations and Appendices

1 Introduction

> **real ale**, a name for draught (or bottled) beer brewed from traditional ingredients. matured by secondary fermentation in the container from which it is dispensed. and served without the use of extraneous carbon dioxide.
>
> Oxford English Dictionary (second edition)

This book is not another eulogy of British ale: most of the tastes described are nasty ones. It is a book offering practical advice on running a pub cellar and serving quality beer.

Fifteen years ago there were 70,000 pubs in Britain. Now there are 63,000 and falling. Social habits have changed, of course, but the pubs that survive will be the ones offering the best service, including the best beer. In England, over 70% of the beer sold is draught. That is the distinctive feature of the British pub and the core of its customer service.

The 'guest beer' market has had a huge effect on the industry. The 1989 Beer Orders allow licensees of major brewing companies to sell a draught beer of their choice. There are few tied houses these days which do not offer an alternative draught beer.

The opening up of the tied house market has encouraged the proliferation of small breweries. Over 300 have opened up in 15 years; over 60 opened in 1995 alone.

So we have the choice, but what about the quality? A selection of badly kept beers is no real choice at all.

Licensees too often have little cellar training, and do not now how to deal with unfamiliar beers.

The trade has responded by making many beers much simpler to handle in the cellar, usually by completing conditioning and maturation in the brewery. Few are the beers which require long periods of cellaring before they are fit for sale. But fewer still are the breweries who label their casks with instructions as how best to prepare and serve their beers. Table 4 attempts to fill some of this knowledge gap.

This book follows two editions of Cellarmanship; my thanks are due to Pat O'Neill who wrote and designed them. Many words and pictures in the present volume are his. Pat would not be one to solicit a title, but he has something more important: the recognition of his peers. He is known to thousands of CAMRA members as *Pat O'Spile*, the man who padded round Alexandra Palace whilst others slept, ensuring that the lifeblood of Great British Beer Festivals would be ready and waiting for the Great British Public.

Ivor Clissold

2 What Real Ale Is

All beers are produced in roughly the same way. Fermentable grains – usually malted barley – are mixed (mashed) with hot water (liquor) to convert the starch into sugars, then boiled. Hops are added early in the boil for bitterness. Aromatic flavours come from adding hops late in the boil or infusing the hot wort through a bed of hops.

The wort is run into fermenting vessels and yeast is added to start fermentation. The yeast multiplies as it consumes the sugars and produces alcohol and carbon dioxide.

After fermentation, different beers are subject to different processes.

Maturation: most beers are kept by the brewery for at least a week to mature in bulk tanks, or in the cask.

Bright and keg beers are chilled to form the yeast and sediment into lumps, to be removed by filtration. Keg beers are also pasteurised for a longer shelf life. Both are put into kegs to be served under gas pressure, as air would make them vulnerable to infection and oxidation.

Draught beers are decanted (racked) into casks. They continue to ferment slowly as the yeasts feed on the remaining fermentable sugars (secondary fermentation). Some beers are given a shot of primings (sugar solution) to produce natural condition, bubbles and a frothy head. Finings are also added to clarify the beer.

Some draught beers are filtered after fermentation, then given a measured shot of yeast (re-seeded) to reduce sediment in the cask and ensure a controlled secondary fermentation. A handful of hops are added to the cask (dry hopping) by some brewers for extra aroma.

In the cellar

Real ale is still alive, and cellaring has to be seen as a continuation of the process initiated by the brewer (Figure 1 below).

Good cellar practice for real ale means, in brief:

- Create a hygienic and temperature controlled environment
- Store the cask so it doesn't move
- Wait for the finings to clarify the beer
- Conclude the maturation process
- Vent off CO_2 pressure caused by secondary fermentation
- Tap the cask, check the quality of the beer and serve if OK
- Tilt the cask to enable all the clear beer to be used
- Seal the empty cask and clean the fittings

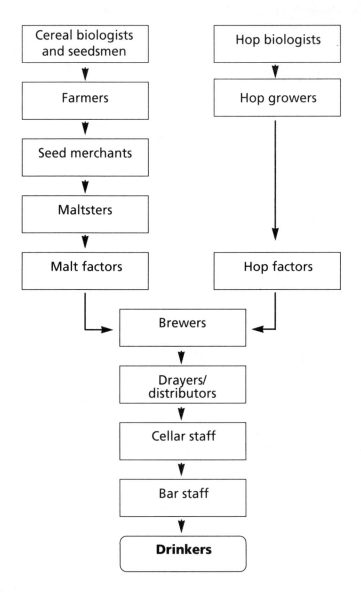

Figure 1: The beer chain

3 Naming of Parts

No trade is without its jargon, and beer is no exception. A number of expressions are not covered by the second edition of the *Oxford English Dictionary*. Appendix 7 gives a round-up of beer related vocabulary.

Casks

Cellar work is mainly concerned with handling containers of draught beer, or *casks*. Processed beers come in *kegs.* A few brewers still use oak casks, but most names apply to the wooden, aluminium and stainless steel varieties.

A wooden cask comprises:

Staves, which are shaped planks which form the body of the cask. One of these is especially wide (the bung stave) to take the bung hole bush, which will hold the shive.

The top head, made from planks fitted horizontally, enabling the bottom D-shaped plank (cant) to be drilled for the keystone bush, which will hold the tap.

The back head, which is plain with the planks fitted vertically (middles to bung stave).

Hoops, which secure the heads in their grooves and hold the staves together.

The ends of the staves, where they overlap the heads, is called the chimb (pronounced chime). The sections between the chimb and the pitch (belly) are called quarters.

Metal casks are made from two castings welded together. Bereft of hoops, staves, middles and cants, the wooden cask terminology still applies.

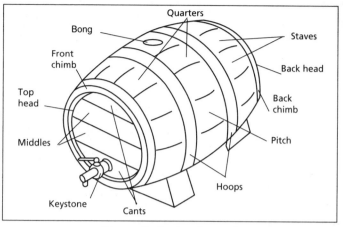

Figure 2: Parts of a cask

Traditional cask sizes are derived from the 36 gallon barrel, which is an imperial bulk size of two gross (288) pints. They are:

4.5 gallons	Pin (quite rare)
9 gallons	Firkin
18 gallons	Kilderkin ('Kil')
36 gallons	Barrel
54 gallons	Hogshead (rare)

Two metric sizes are commonly in use: 50 litres (11 gallons) and 100 litres (22 gallons). These are called by their imperial size, 'an eleven' or 'a twenty-two'. Most of the breweries using them price their beer by the barrel (36 gallons) and then price each metric container by its approximate gallon equivalent. For cask weights and dimensions see Appendix 1.

Cask is the generic name for a draught beer container. A *barrel* is specifically a 36 gallon cask, and gives the unit of measurement which most brewers use to convey their plant capacity, quote prices and measure production. The hectolitre (100 litres) is also in use for excise reporting purposes, and will become the standard in the EU single market.

The word *barrel* should be used only when referring to a 36 gallon cask or to the unit of brewery measurement. For other container sizes, either use their proper names or refer to a specific size of *cask*.

The traditional cask names, and the word cask itself, are used when referring to cask conditioned ales. Keg beers, lagers and processed ciders tend to come in metric containers, but these are always known as either kegs or tubs. In the smaller sizes, kegs are usually parallel sided rather than the traditional bellied cask shape. Some containers – styled 'converter kegs' – have both a centre and a keystone hole in the front head, one of which is closed out of use with a torqued plug.

You may also come across two other metric sizes: 25 litres, which is about 5.5 gallons, and 150 litres, which is about about 33 gallons.

Finally, there's the 'polypin', a collapsible plastic bag within a cardboard box. It holds four and a half gallons. Polypins were developed for the take-home trade, and are not really suitable for cask conditioned beer since they cannot be vented easily and a lively beer could burst the bag. Their ideal use is for re-racked ('bright') beer designed for quick consumption.

Pipework (lines)

Beer is either piped up to the counter or drawn straight from a tap in the cask – 'gravity' dispense. To connect to a line, the tap needs a threaded spout and a face to mate with the pipe termination (tail). The two faces are not usually in direct contact; a washer and a hop filter interpose. Holding the joint assembly together is a union (burr) which cups behind the tail and screws onto the tap thread.

Dispensers

The pipe terminates with another tail and burr at a beer engine or, via an electric pump, to a dispense font.

A quick look round the cellar

This is just to familiarise you with the general arrangement.

1   Thermometer (Chapter 32)

2   Cellar tidy (Chapter 32)

3   Horizontally stillaged cask on standby (Chapter 6)

4   Horizontally stillaged cask in use

5   Tap (Chapters 10 and 27)

6   Tail, burr and hop filter (Chapter 28)

7   Wedge or chock

8   Vented shive (Chapter 8)

9   Stooper (Chapter 11)

10 Vertically stillaged cask in use (Chapter 12)

11 Extractor (Chapter 12)

12 Y union

13 Beer lines to counter (Chapter 28)

14 Sump

15 Sink

16 Hose

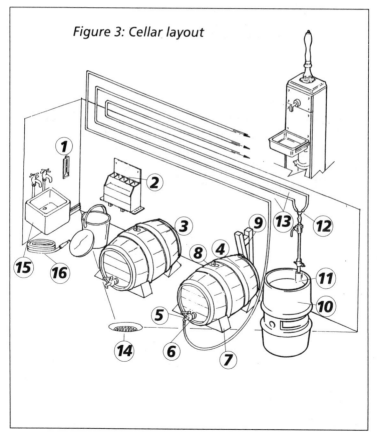

Figure 3: Cellar layout

4 Ordering

While a cask of real ale is undergoing secondary fermentation there will be a slightly positive pressure of CO_2 in the cask, acting as a barrier against airborne bugs and oxygen. As the beer is consumed there is progressively less beer in the cask and less CO_2 being produced to fill the increasing headspace. Air will be drawn into the cask to replace the beer drawn off. The oxygen in this air will be taken up by the beer, causing oxidation and allowing growth of any aerobic yeasts or bacteria like lactobacilli that may be present. Spores of these spoilage organisms may also be drawn in with the air and colonise the surface of the beer. The carbon dioxide, dissolved in the beer and giving it its 'condition', will start to be lost through the exposed surface of the beer.

All of these detrimental mechanisms continue inexorably whilst the cask is in service. Usually it takes two days for the beer to go flat. In a clean cellar, sourness should not be evident (except in the last pint or two) for several days.

The beer will often continue to drink well until the infected surface level drops sufficiently to be drawn out of the tap. That is why beer can go 'off' so suddenly, in the cleanest of cellars. If a customer complains, it is wrong to say 'everyone else is drinking it'. They are not: the pint pulled off previously was probably quite OK.

Rate of change

The rate of change is influenced by many factors, including temperature, cleanliness, type and strength of beer. Perhaps most important, however, is the combination of cask size and rate of beer usage. This is because many changes depend upon the ratio of the volume of the beer to its surface area.

The smaller the surface a given volume of beer presents to the air, the longer it will last. The last four and a half gallons in the bottom of a barrel will deteriorate much more quickly than the same amount in a full pin.

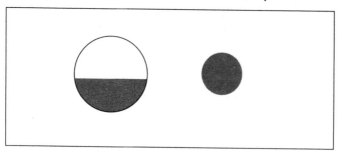

Figure 4: Equal volumes in different sized casks

In general, with two casks of differing sizes, emptying within the same time (i.e. at differing serving rates), the beer in the larger will keep better. Conversely, when emptying at the same serving rate (i.e. taking differing times), then the beer in the smaller will be the better.

Beers that need cellar maturation seem to acquire superior flavours when matured in larger containers.

With ordinary milds and bitters, choose a cask size so that the beer is on sale no more than two days. Strong bitters can stand three or four days, and barley wines or old ales will normally last a week. High temperatures, bad hygiene and over-venting will reduce these times, whilst scrupulous cellar work – maximising hard spiling, keeping the air clean and the temperature correct – can extend them.

The problem can be greatly reduced by ensuring that real ale is ordered in the correct size of cask to suit the volume of trade. If trade increases, you can almost halve your cellar work by doubling the size of the casks. Bigger casks also take up less space pro rata.

Where there are two dispense points for the same beer, it is better to use a single cask with either a double-outlet tap or a Y-connector in the line. This not only allows a bigger cask to be used up in the same time as two smaller ones, but also saves on stillage space, enabling more of the beer stock to be stillaged at the same time.

Health and safety legislation, combined with the growth of the guest beer market, have pushed many brewers into using the firkin as the industry standard size. Most brewers supply their beers in a selection of cask sizes without price differentials. This practice encourages the retailer to select sizes best suited to the trade.

'Nines' and 'eighteens' are the two sizes in most common use today, with 'thirty-sixes' (barrels) still used a lot in the North. For dimensions and weights see Appendix 2.

5 Receiving

If you think safety is expensive, try an accident! Being in a cellar when casks are coming down the drop can be a bit like the Blitz. Clean the area where the fresh casks are to be stillaged. Have a scout round before the delivery to make sure the drop is clear, the floor is dry, and pipes and other obstructions are cleared out of the way. Something as small as a bottle-top can be enough to twist an ankle.

You will not normally be expected to unload, but if you have to, remember that casks look hefty but are easily damaged. They should always be off-loaded onto a cushion and never allowed to roll down steps. Use ropes, pulley and lifts where available.

Before you accept a delivery, check you got what you ordered. Give casks the once-over for leaks. The usual sites are where the cask changes dimension, leaving an edge to be damaged by dropping the cask. If the leak is round the keystone or shive, see if it can be cured by driving home with a mallet. If not, the seating is damaged and the cask should be rejected.

Keeping clean

If you are at all cellar-proud, dirty casks will not feature on your gantries. Wash them down, but avoid obliterating the labels (usually on the front head).

Casks are often delivered with considerable mould growth on the outside of shives and keystones. This does not indicate trouble within, merely how quickly mould will develop upon spilt beer. But it is a source of possible infection and, if left, will be pushed into the cask when spiling and tapping. Use a small brush to scrub the keystone and shive with cleaning solution, then rinse.

There are health and safety regulations which prevent even the muscle-bound lifting casks alone. Get some help

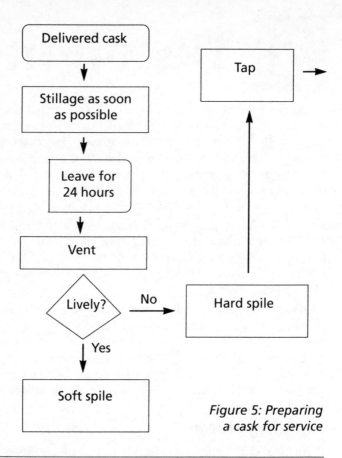

Figure 5: Preparing a cask for service

and assess how you are going to do the task before you start. A cask is quite easy to roll and steer, once you get the knack of letting its weight do the work.

All casks should have a paper label giving a date or brew serial number (gyle number). Use them in chronological order. One delivery can often contain casks with beer of different ages.

After the delivery, remember to close and lock the drop or access point. The dropway and cellar floor will need a wash down.

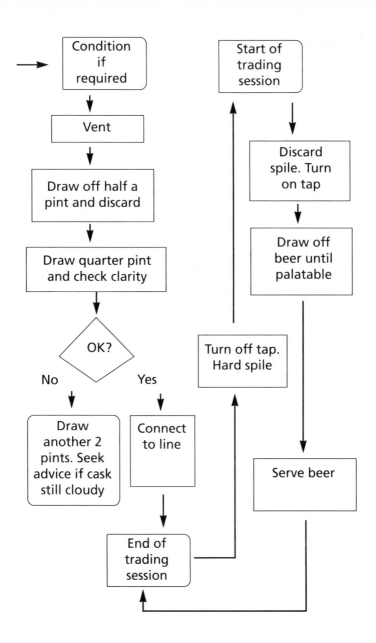

6 Stillaging

Cask conditioned beer has to be set up in its serving position and then left undisturbed until the cask is empty. The cask has to be supported so it does not rock or shake. The way to do this is to support it on three points only. Three legs are much more stable than four. (An alternative system that stands the casks on end is discussed in Chapter 12.)

If the cask is to go on the floor, a shelf or counter, timber wedges (chocks or scotches) should be used. A suitable size is about 150 mm x 90 mm on the sides and 75 mm wide. The timber is best left in its sawn state to give a good grip.

Support the cask on three chocks, two at the front and one at the rear. Always place the chocks with the long side as the base. Make sure the bilge of the cask is lifted completely clear of the surface, so the cask rests only on the three chocks. When setting up on a slippery surface (plastic laminates are especially bad) a cloth or bar towel should be stretched under the chocks first, with all the chocks on the same piece of material so that any tendency to slip is resisted by the tension in the cloth.

| Right | Wrong | Tilted cask |

Figure 6: Chocking

A permanent stillage (also referred to as a rack, horse, thrawl or gantry) should not require loose wedges. It is better to have permanently attached blocks. The usual arrangement is to have two substantial horizontal timber beams as the basis of the stillage and to fix, to the rear beam, wooden blocks with curved cut-outs of a diameter less than that of any cask to be used (about 300-500 mm).

With this system the cask is supported at three points: at the back by the horns of the block, while the front quarters rest on the beam. The levels of the beams are set so the casks are correctly tilted for the final serving position. If less tilt is required, a wooden batten can be inserted under the front quarters.

Another common form of permanent stillage is a brick, concrete or even iron construction either as two walls replacing the timbers mentioned above, or like a shelf against the cellar wall, usually between 300 mm and 450 mm high. These can disturb the beer by transmitting low frequency vibrations from nearby traffic and machinery. Timber beams or rubber matting laid along the upper surface make effective insulators.

A permanent stillage requires the labour of lifting the casks on and off (without disturbing the others). The casks are easier to tap, but this is a one-off job and it would be easier to crouch while tapping. The structure also has nooks and corners which are not easily cleaned.

The latest stillaging innovations are proprietary steel frameworks (sometimes two-storied with mechanical lifting devices) which hold casks on a pallet. The initial capital expenditure for these is high but the two-storey types, combined with the auto-tilting devices mentioned in Chapter 11, are very efficient and economical with space.

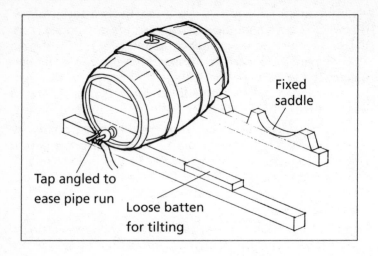

Figure 7: Permanent stillage

Unless you are going to fill glasses directly from the cask, casks can be set up directly on the floor, using either loose chocks or small individual frames, but take care to insert the tap with the pipe outlet to one side rather than straight down. Cleaning the floor while casks are stillaged upon it is impossible without splashing the tap and possibly tainting the beer with steriliser or disinfectant.

If space is available, put casks into the serving position on delivery. If this is not practicable, store them on their sides, bung uppermost and wedged to prevent inadvertent movement.

If you move a cask gently you will inevitably rouse sediment without disturbing the finings, so the beer will never clear. If a cask has to be moved, give it a good roll round the cellar before re-stillaging. Then make sure you leave enough time for the finings to work before the beer is required for use.

7 Records

Even if you run a one-person cellar, it is important you work systematically. Misfortune – or even fortune – may prevent your appearance one day, and quality will be at risk unless you leave some indication of what you have been doing. This is not only of help to others: we all have our reveries and lacunae of absent-mindedness.

Many cellars use only one brewery's beers, so tapping, venting and maturation is always the same process and everyone should know the routine. About the only recorded information necessary is to chalk NEXT on the next cask to be used. But if you are dealing with a range of ales or many staff, stick a record label on each cask. That way others can see when it was spiled and what the condition was. As well as helping you and your colleagues serve good beer, if things go wrong it is good evidence to show to the brewery.

Beer name:	Ancient & Modern			
Delivery date:	28-2			
Set up date:	28-2			
Date	Time	Qty	Cond	Spile
29-2	1030	Full	Lively	Soft
29-2	1600	7	L	S
1-3	0800	7	Quiet	H
4-3	1320		-	On sale
4-3	11.30	5	-	H
5-3	11.30	1	-	H
6-3	1300	MT		

Figure 8: Cask record slip

8 Spiling

The shive in a traditional cask contains a central section – a tut – which can be punched through, allowing:

- CO_2 to be vented off
- Air to be let in, so beer can be drawn off without creating an airlock.

It is better not to use a hard spile to vent casks. Hard spiles are too short for the job, and you risk bruised fingers when the mallet is applied.

A steel punch is the best tool. The cheapest form is an old engine valve about 150 mm long with a 10 mm diameter stem. Valves are made of hardened steel and should be used only with a mallet. Cellar suppliers can provide a purpose-made job, see Appendix A1.

Casks that have just been delivered and set up, especially if they are warm, are best left for at least 4 hours before venting, as the beer is likely to be very lively and venting could be messy and wasteful. If gantry space is available, set casks up into the serving position several days before venting.

Take precautions if you expect the beer to be lively. If there are two people, one can use the venting tool and the other can be ready with the soft spile, held immediately next to the shive, to be instantaneously inserted as the tool is withdrawn. It is also advisable to cover the venting tool with a bar towel to prevent hops being sprayed onto the ceiling!

When it is expected that the beer will be lively, the use of a proprietary venting spile with a controllable draw-off tube will save mess.

Clean up any spillage as soon as possible. Beer puddles are potential farms for wild and rogue yeasts and bacteria.

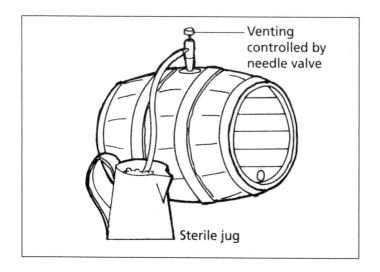

Figure 9: Controlled vent plug

The warmer the beer, the less CO_2 it will absorb at a given pressure. So if the beer is above ideal temperature, the pressure has to be increased to give condition. The pressure can be increased by not venting the cask, allowing CO_2 produced from the secondary fermentation to build up and remain in solution. Releasing the gas from what has become a pressurised container demands care in the use of a process known as tap venting.

1. Stillage the cask as normal. Make sure the shive and keystone are firmly in position.

2. A few hours before serving tap the cask (see Chapter 10) with the tap set half-open to allow pressure to escape and to avoid sending a disturbing bubble through the beer. Close the tap once driven home.

3. Open the tap slightly and test for clarity. The beer will be turbid so let it settle before judging.

4. Connect the beer to the line. Gradually open the tap and allow the cask pressure to push the beer into the line. If serving by gravity, run the beer into a jug and serve it from there.

5. When the pressure has equalised, vent the cask and continue as normal.

Tap venting is not without its risks. Excess pressure can blow the tap out of a plastic keystone, and rapid venting can disturb the sediment. However, beer with high condition is much more palatable than flat beer, especially if warm.

In temperature-controlled cellar conditions with a regular throughput of well-rested casks, beer loss when spiling should be minimal. If beer loss persists, then use a controlled venting spile. In this case the beer blown off during venting can be collected in a sterilised jug and returned to the cask, but see Chapter 14.

Secondary complete

Beers are increasingly delivered with secondary fermentation all but complete. Venting them releases hardly any gas. These beers should be hard spiled directly after venting, to retain what condition they have. Table 5 gives some idea of what to expect from various beers.

After venting the cask with the venting tool, stand by with a soft spile. Tap it in if there is any sign of activity: sometimes nothing happens for 10 seconds or so, then a rumbling is heard and a geyser results if the spile is not tapped home smartly. Do not wallop soft spiles into the spile hole or you will squash up their pores and defeat their object, which is a gradual release of CO_2.

The best soft spiles are made of bamboo and are easily recognised by their short, stubby shape and the shiny, dark outer bamboo skin. The fibrous inner texture is quite visible. Other types are made from coarse grained softwood and from hard spiles with narrow longitudinal saw-cuts. If in doubt about a batch of spiles, put one in the lips and blow hard: a soft spile will be noticeably porous.

There is a great variation in the porosity of soft spiles and the brittleness – and porosity – of hard spiles. Bamboo has been mentioned, but 'semi-soft' spiles are available, made from ash which will not resist high pressure, thus acting as an auto-spile.

Guest beers

If you deal with a number of guest beers, supplies of spiles, shives and keystones can come from a number of brewery sources. While these are free, it can be an advantage to use one supplier so you get to know the behaviour of their products. Table 4 gives manufacterers.

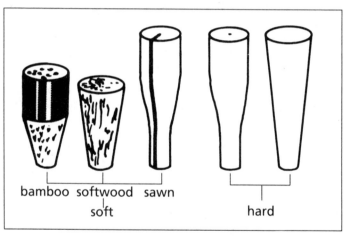

Figure 10: Spiles

If the beer is in serving condition, all you should get when the cask is vented is a sharp burst of gas, then silence. Fit a hard spile, and remove it carefully when the beer is to be served.

A cask with a soft spile must be checked at least twice a day. Remove the spile and check that the spile pores have not become blocked with yeast, preventing gas release. If you have plenty of spiles, fit a new spile each time you check the cask. When there is no activity, fit a hard spile.

Keep the hard spile firmly in place when the cask is not in service, but withdraw it completely when the cask is in use. A spile left loosely in the shive can get sucked back into the hole by air entering as beer is drawn off, blocking the hole and creating an airlock. This only becomes obvious in the bar when the hand-pull starts getting stiff and springs back after pulling. By this time there is a partial vacuum in the cask and removal of the spile will cause a sudden pressure change which may disturb the sediment and give cloudy beer. In this event, ease the spile very gently, listening to the slow inflow of air until the pressures equalise. If a hand-pull suddenly exhibits this symptom, especially just after changing a cask, the cause is almost always the cask tap inadvertently being left closed. If so, gentleness is the approach: open the tap very slowly, or the sudden rush of beer into the line may cause disturbance and raise the sediment.

Where a beer is in infrequent service – such as a firkin of winter ale on the bar – the best practice is to keep the hard spile in all the time and loosen it each time a pint is drawn.

9 Conditioning

The term 'conditioning' covers the chemical, biological and physical changes that occur in beer from the time it leaves the brewery fermenting vessel to when it is served.

'Conditioning' is not the same as 'condition', the amount of carbon dioxide in the beer. This is discussed in more detail in Chapter 21.

The main processes that concern us are *secondary fermentation*, *dropping bright* (settling, clearing or fining) and *maturation*.

After primary fermentation in the brewery's fermenting vessel, the beer is transferred either to a racking tank, which feeds the cask-filling stations, or to a maturation tank, where the beer begins conditioning. Secondary fermentation is a gentler process than primary, because most fermentable sugars are metabolised by yeast in the early stage of fermentation.

Secondary fermentation should be substantially over by the time that the cask has finished venting. Of course, a biological process does not turn off like a switch, and some fermentation continues until the cask is empty.

During secondary fermentation, the residual yeast, left in the beer after racking into the cask, continues to attack the remaining sugars, generating more alcohol, carbon dioxide and flavour by-products. Secondary fermentation can account for a one or two degree drop in final gravity, yielding around a 0.1% increase in alcohol by volume.

Secondary fermentation materially affects the beer's flavour. Fermentation in the cask produces carbon dioxide which dissolves in the beer, giving it 'condition', without which it would be flat, lifeless and unpleasant to drink.

Venting and soft spiling before the cask is put into service allows excess gas, generated during secondary fermentation, to escape. During this time the cask must be left undisturbed in its final position, allowing the finings to coagulate the sediment, leaving the beer clear (bright), preferably brilliantly clear (polished).

Finings are made from isinglass – the swim bladders of fish. These are almost pure collagen which is dispersed into a colloidal state by steeping the bladders in a dilute natural acid such as tartaric, citric or malic acid. This slimy, but invaluable, substance causes all the yeast cells and any other solid particles to clump together and fall to the bottom of the cask. Usually, a proportion also *rises* to the surface of the beer.

These two forms of 'sediment' are known as the 'bottom break' and the 'top break'. It is in large part the top break sediment, floating on the surface of the beer, that produces the cloudiness in the final pint drawn out of the cask.

Maturation

Maturation includes all the other changes that the beer undergoes in the cask. Amongst these are the slow interactions of the many fermentation products producing other chemical complexes, take-up of flavours from any dry hops added at the time of racking, elution of volatile substances by the carbon dioxide coming out of solution, and the reduction of any oxygen still present.

The time required for conditioning and maturation is highly variable. Strong ales and barley wines will improve in cask for several months. The bottled Prize Old Ale brewed by Gales is conditioned for a year before bottling and then kept in bottle for another couple of months before distribution. Conversely, beers of a low gravity – milds and light bitters – will be at their best within a week or so of racking.

Casks seldom come with instructions, so a cellarer handling a strange brand cannot tell whether the beer has been held at the brewery until secondary fermentation and conditioning has finished, or if this has been left wholly or partly to the retailer. This can make the difference between almost immediate sale and a week or two of storage. Appendix 5 gives recommendations as to when beers are ready to serve, and, if different, when they reach optimum maturity.

Appendix 5 also indicates whether a cask of beer will improve with keeping. Much depends on the brewing process: how much of the starch in the mash tun was converted to mono or disaccharide sugar which the yeast can easily digest; the quantity of polysaccharides remaining which the yeast may slowly break down; the amount and viability of the yeast and the temperature.

Keeping beer in the cask to come to optimum condition is expensive for the brewer and the licensee, tying up capital, casks and storage space. Hence the trend amongst brewers to send out beers that will settle and can be sold within hours of delivery. Brewery maturation does reduce the variation of flavour, seen as one of the great characteristics of real ale.

One practical problem for the cellarman is to know exactly how old beer is on delivery. Although most brewers put a date label on their casks, this is not universal, nor are all based on the same method. For example, most dates refer to the date of racking (filling the cask), but some labels indicate the date of shipment from a depot, the date the cask was fined, or a 'best before' date (BBD). Most brewers mark their casks with 'gyle' numbers (brew serial numbers), but some use codes, the significance of which are known only to themselves. In a busy cellar this can cause confusion. It is advisable to record the delivery dates on casks, so at least their cellar age will be known.

The time taken for beer to vent excess carbon dioxide gas and drop bright is also subject to considerable variations, generally longer for higher gravity and sweeter beers. Some beers will vent and clear in as little as four or five hours, whilst others can take a week. As a generalisation, one should plan for most beers to have at least two days from venting to start of service, and for strong ales, three to four days.

10 Tapping

There are three views on when a cask should be tapped. One is as soon as the cask is vented, a second is a day or so before use, and a third is only when the cask is required for service.

It is better to tap sooner rather than later, if only because you have more leeway.

- You can pick your own time to do the task
- Tapping immediately after venting turns two jobs into one
- It doesn't matter if the cask is disturbed.
- Leaky taps or keystones can be easily changed.
- Skilled staff are not required to tap and change casks.

Early tapping allows sediment to settle in the tap, but this is drawn off with the first sample.

Tapping some hours before use is advocated by many brewers. It allows for a degree of disturbance and it means that a systematic schedule can be adopted (for example, tapping the day's requirement each morning before opening).

You will need a mallet with a head weighing at least one pound. A weighty rubber or composition mallet is fine: the surface will tend to chip, but this is preferable to the mushrooming of a wooden mallet-head. With a good mallet the experienced cellarman should be able to get the tap in place most times with one or two blows. Never use a metal hammer: it is dangerous and will ruin the tap.

1. Remove the spile to ensure there has been no pressure build up, then fit a hard spile.

2. If you are tapping early, leave the tap closed. If the beer has settled, set the tap half-open to avoid sending a disturbing bubble into the cask.

3. Hold the tap, making sure your hand is not on the part of the spigot that will disappear into the keystone. Hold the spigot of the tap against the recessed centre of the keystone: this will need to be done firmly if using a plastic tap, as they tend to bounce when hit. The tap will need to be vertical if dispensing by gravity, otherwise give consideration to the direction of the beer line so the tap can be angled to assist connection and beer flow.

4. Using a heavy mallet, drive the tap in with 1-3 vigorous blows. Close the tap if open.

5. Check for leaks in the tap or the keystone. If beer is seeping out between keystone and tap, another blow with the mallet will stop it, but if you have been over-energetic and split the keystone, or if the leak is from the tap, a replacement must be fitted at once: see Chapter 13.

After tapping a cask that is to go directly into service, remove the spile and draw off about one third of a pint and discard it. The next third should be substantially clear, and from there on the beer should be servable. Use a sleeve glass for taking samples – the clarity is much better judged. If the beer is still cloudy after a couple of pints have been drawn, don't waste any more time – or beer – and either contact the brewer (or supplier) or see Appendix 6.

Casks tapped earlier should be tested in the same way before use to clear the sediment from the tap. Never connect the beer line until the beer runs clear and tastes good in the cellar.

When connecting the line to the tap, fit a hop filter to the mating face of the tail, inside the burr. This will not only keep floaters out of customers' glasses, but also will help prevent stray strigs or hop leaves preventing beer engine valves from seating correctly. Sometimes the tail/burr/tap face combination will require a washer as well as the hop filter; other combinations may mean you will have to take a slice off the (fibre) face of the filter to get the burr onto the tap.

Tighten the burr firmly by hand. With a good washer and an undamaged tap it should not be necessary to tighten the line with a spanner. This makes cask changing much easier.

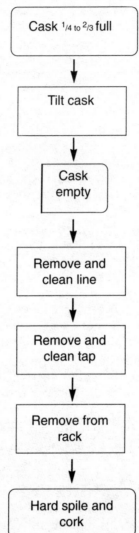

Figure 11:
Cask disposal

Cask 1/4 to 2/3 full

Tilt cask

Cask empty

Remove and clean line

Remove and clean tap

Remove from rack

Hard spile and cork

11 Tilting

If the cask has been stillaged horizontally it will need to be tilted (stooped) so the last of the beer can be drawn off. This should be done well before the flow reduces to a dribble or the pump starts pulling air.

1. Tilt the cask when it is between a half and a third full. Do this after a trading session, in case any disturbance causes the sediment to rise.

2. Tilt in one slow, uninterrupted movement to the final position. Do not pull the cask up beyond its intended angle and then drop it back – this sloshes the beer and disturbs the sediment.

3. The finished position should leave the cask with the back chimb the same height as the shive.

When tilting a cask supported on chocks it is best to lean over from the front of the cask, lift the back rim gently with one hand, slide the rear chock forward with the other hand, using your chest to steady the cask's forward movement.

Do not over-tilt. There is nothing to be gained by tilting more than to the point where the rear chimb of the cask is horizontal with the shive. Too large a tilt will cause the sediment to collect around the tap and the tap spigot will protrude above the surface of the beer where, as the beer runs out, it will pull in floating 'sediment' (the 'top break'), resulting in greater wastage.

Many cellarmen set casks to their final serving angle at the start. Whether this is practicable depends on the type of cask, the amount of sedimentation and the degree of filling achieved by the brewery. (Casks completely full to the shive will lose beer if tilted straight away.) Extraction of two or three pints allows almost any cask to be tilted, but full casks are of course heavier and more difficult to move gently.

Figure 12: Tilt angle

There are a number of mechanical contrivances (stoopers) that make tilting easier, ranging from complicated screw jacks to simple notched wooden sticks. Mason's supply a wooden 'A' frame arrangement with notches on one outer edge (Appendix 1).

Self-tilting stillages contain a cradle to carry the cask which pivots on a frame. Biasing springs or weights allow the cradle to tilt the cask slowly and automatically as the beer is used up and it gets lighter. Two things to watch, though. If the pivots rust the cradles will snatch. The biasing spring or weight has to be correct for the size of cask, but they are usually colour-coded and easily swapped.

12 Vertical Extraction

Stillaged casks use a lot of space, and handling needs considerable strength. The answer to both problems is to use vertical extraction. Instead of the cask being stillaged horizontally, it is stood on end, saving space and lifting. Casks can be placed anywhere in the cellar by the draymen and used without moving them again.

The cask is stillaged on its back chimb, keystone uppermost. A tube is inserted into the cask through the keystone, extending towards the bottom of the cask (i.e. the back head). At the top a screw connection takes the beer line. A cock in this head allows the beer to be closed off, as with a normal tap.

The extractor tube is inserted through a shank driven into the keystone exactly like a tap. This body has a threaded upper part, which has either a sealing cap or plug fitted, or an annular clamping ferrule when the extractor is in place.

For a traditional cask, with keystone, you need an extractor shank as shown in Figure 14. The cask is broached as follows.

1.   Place a small wedge under the bottom chimb to tip the beer away from the keystone.

2.   Fit the blanking plug to the shank and drive it into the keystone with a mallet.

3.   Vent the cask via the venting cock. If the beer is lively a tube can be fitted from the cock to a container to catch the fob, but keep the end above the height of the cock to avoid siphoning. The tube can be fitted

with a soft spile, if required. After venting the cock should be turned off, like normal hard spiling.

4. To 'tap', remove the blanking plug from the shank and insert a clean extractor tube until it touches the bottom of the cask. Withdraw the tube an inch and lock in position.

5. Carefully remove the wedge from under the cask and place on the opposite side to tilt beer towards the keystone. This saves tipping later.

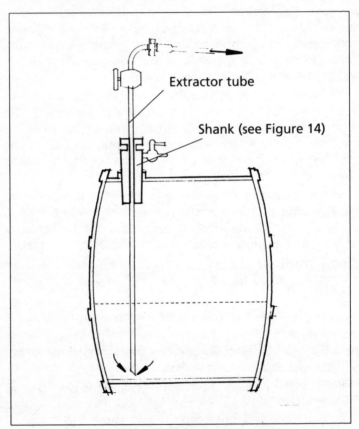

Extractor tube

Shank (see Figure 14)

Figure 13: Vertical extraction

To use the extractor system, you need about three shanks and two blanking plugs for each extractor tube in use.

With the shank extractor system, beer can be served somewhat sooner after venting than with a conventionally stillaged cask. Beer clears generally from the top down, so the upper part of the cask will generally be clear before the bottom, possibly within hours of being vented. By inserting the tube only part way (the clamping ferrule allows the tube to be set firmly at any depth), the top beer can be served whilst the bottom of the cask is still clearing. This is not without problems, not least in that the beer may be young and 'green', but it does give flexibility to help meet unexpected increases in sales.

The shank extractor system can give precise control of bottoms. The process above describes the usual one inch setting. But much depends on the equipment. The amount of bottoms remaining in the cask is determined by the height of the *top holes* (the first to draw air) in the extraction tube, above the end of the tube. With some trial and error, the length of the filter end cap on the extraction tube can be varied to suit the amounts of sediment to be found in particular types of beer.

Having fitted an extractor it is difficult to take a beer sample before putting a cask into service. However, a beer sampling tube – a calibrated pipette – can be bought to extract a beer sample. It can also be used as a dipstick. The pipette is inserted into the cask, then the thumb is used to close the top end of the tube, forming an airlock which allows the beer inside the tube to be retained whilst the pipette is withdrawn from the cask. The thumb is released and the beer is decanted into a glass for the usual quality checks. The tube cannot be used for both purposes at once, as it must be kept at least 1 inch off the bottom to extract a sample unsullied by bottoms, whereas in dipstick mode it must touch the bottom to give an accurate reading.

Extractors are difficult to clean without the right gear. A long trough is needed so the tubes can be soaked in cleaner, and a 40 inch long ale extractor brush to clean the insides.

Some breweries package cask conditioned beer in converted kegs which have had their integral spear sawn off to allow for bottoms. With these a modified keg clip-on head is locked onto the cask which mates with the extractor tube already fitted. Again there is a venting tap and a connection to the beer line. Providing the normal conditioning and venting principles are observed, this type of container is quite satisfactory for real ale. Of course, the cask does not require tipping with a wedge when connecting up or emptying, the fitting being in the centre. There is no way of adjusting the depth of the extractor tube either.

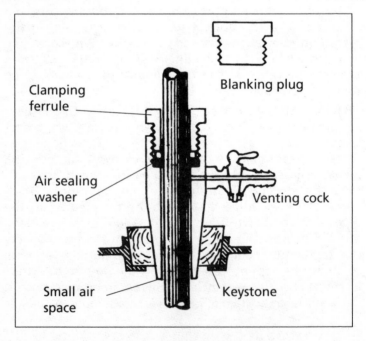

Figure 14: Extractor shank

13 Changing a Tap or Keystone

Sometimes a tap or keystone has to be changed without disturbing the beer. This seems a daunting task to anyone who has not done it before, calling up the vision of an expensive flood. But a tap can be changed without either disturbing the beer or losing more than a few millilitres. Follow these instructions.

1. Hard spile the cask tightly. This produces an air-lock that will drastically slow down any beer out-flow.

2. Check you have the appropriate equipment. A bucket below the tap; a mallet; a lever (a large screwdriver is usual); replacement tap; new keystone or cork bung. Check that the new bung or keystone is the right size. There are a number of sizes in use and it is embarrassing to execute the manoeuvre perfectly only to be left holding a keystone in a hole that is 5mm larger!

3. Changing the tap

   a) Gently knock the tap from side to side and up and down while holding the keystone in position. If the keystone becomes loose, re-seat it using the mallet with the lever as a punch. You will be able to feel when the tap becomes quite loose in the keystone and is being held in only by your hand.

   b) Continuing to hold the tap in the keystone,

take a cork bung in the other hand and hold it next to the keystone. Pull the tap straight out and slide the bung over and into the hole in the keystone. Do this in one movement and only a few teaspoonsful of beer will escape.

c) Insert the replacement tap in the normal way, driving it through the corked keystone.

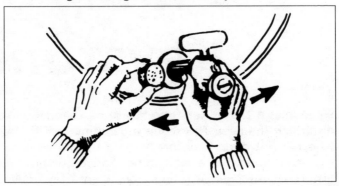

Figure 15: Changing a tap

4. Changing the keystone

a) Push the tap into the keystone very hard then loosen the keystone by knocking the tap up and down and from side to side. You should be able to see the keystone moving in its seat whilst being still tight on the tap.

b) Once the keystone is loose in the cask but still fast on the tap, pull it out and, in one movement, insert the new keystone and tap it home with a mallet.

c) If possible, leave the new keystone for an hour or so before re-tapping. A new, dry keystone has more propensity to split than one that has been softened by the beer.

These operations are easy with full casks. In partly empty casks the airlock is not so efficient, so the dexterity required increases as the beer decreases.

14 Returning Beer to the Cask

It is always bad practice to return beer to a cask. No matter how clean and well-filtered the beer is, it has been saturated with oxygen which will oxidise the alcohol in the cask. This produces acetaldehyde, giving a sharp, apple taste, and acetic acid (or vinegar). It is not worth risking a cask of wholesome beer for the sake of a couple of pints.

Filtering back is the most common reason for poor quality in traditional beer. Most companies condemn the practice publicly, and the Brewers' Society (now the Brewers and Licensed Retailers Association) are also on record as opposing the return of beer to the cask.

Where filtering back is permitted, rules vary. Guidelines usually say the beer should be filtered into a sterile container and tasted. If this test is satisfactory the beer should then be returned *immediately* via a sterile funnel (tun dish). Alternatively, the sample can be tested first and the filtration then performed directly in the tun dish (Figure 16). A new filter paper must be used every time. The cask should never be less than half full, and the addition should never form more than a tenth of the cask contents.

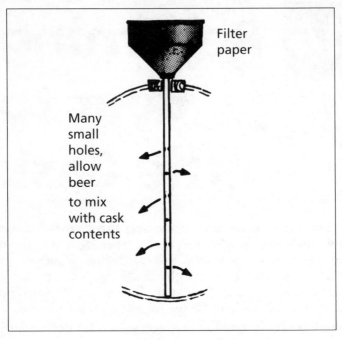

Filter paper

Many small holes, allow beer

to mix with cask contents

Figure 16: Tun dish

Basically, returning beer to the cask is best avoided by other sounder and more efficient cellar techniques. For instance, returning the small amount of beer recovered from an automatic venting spile is not worth the effort expended or the risks incurred. Similarly, rather than returning sound beer drawn off lines prior to their cleaning, it is better to co-ordinate cleaning with cask changes, which saves work.

If beer wastage through pipes is a problem, look at the diameter of the lines. The plastic piping used for draught beer comes in three basic sizes: $5/8$", $1/2$" and $3/8$" internal diameter. The bigger size is very wasteful, holding much more beer per metre than the smaller bores. The lengths of piping per pint of beer are approximately:

⅝" bore	1.6 metres/pint
½" bore	2.5 metres/pint
⅜" bore	4.5 metres/pint

A typical pipe run of ten metres holds over six pints in ⅝" bore but less than two and a quarter pints in ⅜" pipe. Re-piping large bore systems with ⅜" pipe will pay for itself many-fold in savings and quality improvements. The only drawback is marginally heavier resistance on the hand-pulls. Again, returning two pints of beer which has been sitting in lines losing condition is worth neither the time nor the risk.

Too often, when a new cask is put on, one sees one or two gallons drawn off from the pump into a bucket, for later return to the cask. This is avoided by checking the beer in the cellar *before* connecting the cask to the line.

Other common faults are over-tilting casks, so that sediment is drawn into the line, and repeated pulling of the pump to get the last few ounces of beer. Filling the lines with finings and dead yeast, and then having to flush them out with fresh beer, is absurd.

The 'bottoms' of finished casks should never be filtered back. If a significant amount of beer is left, the cask was incorrectly tilted. The sediment, including the 'top break', is a prime source of infection.

Without doubt, the best plan is to concentrate on good beer management. It is a mark of good cellar practice not to need to use a tun dish at all.

15 Temperature

Controlling the temperature of the beer is a vitally important aspect of cellarmanship. The cellar should be maintained at 13-14°C (55-57°F) at all times. A cellar cooler is generally essential in summer and heating in winter.

It is a false economy to skimp on cooling. Running a small unit continually in the summer will result in bills for repair and early replacement which will exceed the extra cost of a bigger unit. The cost of spoiled beer and lost custom is far better spent on better equipment.

To provide winter heat, an electric fan heater (wall-mounted, no trailing leads on damp floors) or an extension from the building's central heating system is recommended. Never use any form of combustion heating in the cellar. A large, easily read thermometer should be hung in the cellar, in a position away from draughts. Use a max/min model so you can be sure the temperature is not fluctuating excessively.

The reason for maintaining a precise and consistent temperature is its effect on the carbon dioxide content of the beer – its condition. The amount of carbon dioxide that remains in the beer after venting, varies inversely with the temperature. Beer kept too cold will be over-gassy, and beer too warm will be flat. In-line coolers ('flash coolers') are of limited use for cask-conditioned beer. If an in-line cooler is used to compensate for a warm cask, flat, insipid beer will result; if it is used to over-cool the beer, a chill haze is likely. The cask itself must be kept at the right temperature.

All storage areas should have temperature control. If beer gets down towards freezing point, it may develop a chill haze, which can be permanent. This haze is precipitated protein, the same as breweries induce when brewery conditioned 'bright beer' is chilled and filtered to remove proteins. A chill haze does not have much effect on beer flavour, but it will deter drinkers through its appearance. (Of course, *removing* the protein by brewery conditioning does impair flavour.)

If beer gets very hot, even for a short time, the result may be disastrous. Above about 22-23°C (72-74°F) finings undergo an irreversible change and become thin and watery, losing the power to coagulate the sediment. If a cask gets to such a temperature, even for a time too short for accelerated biological degradation, there is a real danger that it will never clear.

A further problem with temperature is rapid fluctuation. A cask that is settled and ready to serve can be made cloudy again by any sudden air temperature change causing convection currents to be set up in the beer near the sides of the cask, disturbing the sediment. Localised heat sources or cold draughts can have the same result.

Chapter 16 describes methods of cooling casks other than cellar (ambient) cooling.

16 Cask Cooling

To keep traditional beer in its peak condition, it must be kept at the right temperature. Outside a cooled cellar, other means must be found to keep the beer cool. There are a number of options.

Hire companies can supply powerful chillers in various sizes. Where casks are stillaged under a counter unit or shelf, front covers can be fitted to make a cold air 'tunnel'. The covers should be a good fit, with small cut-outs for the taps to protrude. The inside of the enclosure should be insulated, for instance with expanded polystyrene sheeting. A low powered air cooler will then keep the tunnel down to cellar conditions. There are self-contained units that take one cask, requiring only connection to a power socket.

Immersion, or 'in-cask', coolers are also available (Figure 17). These are tubes which fit into casks through their bung holes (where the shive is normally fitted). Cooled water is circulated through the cooling probe, and beer can be kept at cellar temperature even in a midsummer beer tent. As with the cooling jackets, the water must be cooled to remove the heat being drawn from the cask(s).

Cooling probes are efficient, but they have drawbacks. The most obvious is hygiene. As the probe sits in the beer throughout its service it must be kept meticulously clean and sterilised between casks. To insert the probe, the shive must be removed, the cask being sealed by a rubber moulding at the top of the probe. This is not always perfect, and the beer may lose condition. If the water circulated through the probe is too cold, two problems can arise which may cause cloudy beer. Local chill haze can be produced in the beer around the probe, and temperature differences can set up convection currents that disturb sediment.

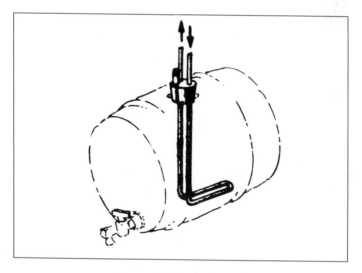

Figure 17: In-cask cooler

Evaporative cooling works well if the water evaporates off the cask. Forget ice: vaporisation is 8 times more efficient at cooling than melting.

Use muslin bags, washed hot to remove cotton oil film. Dry them if you have time: it makes them easier to handle. Slip the bags over the casks. Pinch and snip to uncover the shive. Dampen pieces of absorbent paper and self-adhere them to the cask heads.

Spray the casks with clean water using a clean garden spray. Ensure there is a good air flow to maximise evaporation. Keep the cloths and papers damp.

Figure 18: Evaporative cooling

Keeping the cellar floor wet will help to give some air cooling by evaporation, but this poses risks in the presence of electrical equipment.

In considering beer temperature, one must appreciate the large thermal inertia of a full cask of beer. Whatever the temperature outside a cask, the beer inside the cask will change its temperature by only a few degrees per hour. Temperature peaks can be offset by cooling the room/cellar as much as possible overnight. The beer will stay closer to the average temperature over the whole day.

17 Dispensing

The last step in the process is presenting the glass of beer to the customer. Beers should not be served to look like ice-cream soda.

Traditionally, frothy (nappy) beer was more esteemed in the northern counties. An open, loose type of head can be seen on some worts when they are run into the fermenting vessels from the copper. No amount of foam stabilisers will replicate this head: if the wort doesn't have it, the finished beer won't either. An open, loose froth is a sign of quality ingredients.

Effects of dispense systems

Beer cosmetics did not become a big issue until glass replaced pottery, pewter and leather. This soon led to paler and brighter beers, but the desirability of a head has always seemed to be confined to Yorkshire and its contiguous areas. It was probably the introduction of the Auto-Bak or 'economiser' that created the fashion.

This device connects the beer engine drip tray to the top of the beer pump with a pipe, so that spillage is re-cycled. Once spillage was no longer costly, the habit grew of tightening the rose (sparkler) on the spout to agitate the beer and produce a turbid glassful which slowly cleared to leave a dense head. Almost two pints have to be pulled to produce one in the glass of this texture.

The economiser is frowned upon by environmental health officers: not so much because of the recycling of beer, which does not sustain the growth of pathogens, but because glasses and the hands of serving staff get sluiced in the overspill and can contaminate the beer.

Beer dispensed with such a head undergoes changes in taste, with the head taking up some 10% of the bitterness.

(Try tasting a dollop of froth.) The agitation also whisks most of the dissolved CO_2 out of solution. Although the beer looks lively, it is actually flat, and easier to drink in quantity. Such a drink appealed to workers in steelworks or miners, for instance, who needed to replace fluid by the gallon.

The swan-neck dispense spout was developed as an alternative to the economiser. It is a long spout which reaches to the bottom of the glass. Usually the outlet has an adjustable – even removable – sparkler. Typical sparklers have 16 holes of 0.6 mm diameter, aiding formation of a tight head by forcing the beer through the holes into the bottom of the glass. This causes considerable gas break-out, and because the bubbles are small they have strong surface tension and do not collapse easily. They also rise slowly, supporting the head for longer. The beer tastes smoother and less bitter.

Brewers supplying the 'economiser' areas corrected for the bitterness loss to the head by over-bittering their beers. This became a problem when, like Tetley's, these beers were selected as 'national brands' to be sold countrywide with mass media advertising back-up. Expectation of 'big head' beers (as seen on TV) was met by introducing swan neck dispensers nation-wide.

The problem is that these dispensers are not confined to serving the beers for which they were designed. Gently bittered and aromatically hopped beers should not be subjected to agitated dispense. Slacken or remove the sparkler and fill the glass from the top. If customers demand a head, a perfectly adequate one can be pulled from a short spout with a tight sparkler. The swan-neck is therefore an inconvenience. To replace them, call the manufacturers (see Table 4) who will send you a traditional spout. You will need to specify whether you want a plain spout or one with a tap. (With modern small-bore lines and well-sealing pump valves, there's not much point in having a tap.)

Beer engines

Outside of breweries, the first beer pumps came into use in the late 18th century, when coaching inns had become so big that constant scuttling to the cellar became impractical. Presumably the first models were based on the parish pump. The new century saw banks of them contained in cabinets with fancy curved 'cash-register' fronts and plain backs, being designed to stand against the wall, this being the era before counters. Leather pistons became brass and lead pipes were replaced first partly by glass 'telescopes' then by plastic.

An oddity occasionally seen is the Simcup cask pump. This quarter-pint pull cylinder fits directly onto the cask tap, which has to be fitted upside down. A pull on the handle delivers the beer through a narrow tube with a fishtail end, giving a semblance of a northern head from what is essentially gravity dispense.

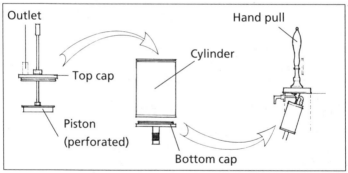

Figure 19: Beer engine

Electric metered pumps

Electric metered pumps are simple and always deliver full measure. The older types had a cylindrical (*Metron*, made by an offshoot of the Metropolitan Gas Board) or spherical (*Spheromatic*, made by Mills Bros.) transparent half-pint chamber on the bar, with a diaphragm inside which pushed out the contents of the chamber whilst being filled again from the other side.

The pump is normally sited in the cellar, which can lead to problems. Though the voltage is low and relatively safe (24V), health and safety experts do not like electrical equipment in proximity to liquid, or wet floors, so many pumps were mounted on the wall. In this position it is not possible to run the system unless the pump is primed by connecting CO_2 to the cask. This rather defeats the object of electric dispense, as the licensees seldom remember, or bother, to disconnect the gas again. Pump motors need regular maintenance such as re-brushing, and this has influenced most companies to switch to gas pumps.

Gas pumps

A recent development, taking the business by storm, is the Flojet, or gas powered pump. Replacing the electric pump, it derives its power from nitrogen, carbon dioxide or compressed air. The gas does not come into contact with the beer and is exhausted to atmosphere. If CO_2 is used it needs to be piped out of the cellar, but CO_2 is expensive, and any sizeable installation would justify an air compressor. Supplied by Stanwell Technic Ltd.

Other dispense equipment

Another metered system comprises a font with a push-button fed from an electric metered supply in the cellar. A push of the button commences delivery of a measured half-pint into the glass.

The majority of today's systems involve electric un-metered ('free-flow') dispensers, but they are not seen as a trendy way to sell cask beers. Like all beer dispensing electric pumps, these operate via a pressure switch. When the tap is opened the pressure falls and the pump kicks in. When it is closed the pressure immediately increases and the pressure switch cuts out the pump.

The oldest dispense system of all – gravity – is making a come-back despite its inconveniences. The beer simply runs out of the tapped cask and into the glass by the clever method discovered by Sir Isaac Newton.

Bar staff

As in any job, so bar staff have to be trained. You should spend an hour or so explaining how the cellar works, what real ale is, and the different types of beer available.

Staff should hold a basic food hygiene certificate, which covers subjects such as food handling, personal hygiene and food poisoning. Courses are available from local councils and training agencies. Perfumed soap, scent or aftershave can have a much stronger effect upon customers and their drinks than the wearer may think.

Glasses

It is best not to mix lined and brim measure glasses in stock, as this confuses bar staff and drinkers. Most drinkers find 24oz glasses too big. Ideal was a 21oz glass which gave a 5mm collar that holds enough froth to make up the full pint. Beer could be served quickly to the top of the glass, settling back to a full measure. Unfortunately this size never went into production after the initial (successful) experiments.

Most pubs stock plain (sleeve) and handled (mug) glasses, though most beer drinkers prefer a sleeve. These were traditionally of conic section, the rim of the glass being the widest point, but the rims are easily chipped when glasses are pushed together. The latest designs prevent rims touching by a bulge (Nonik), or by reversing the cone so the rim is smaller (Tulip and Rio). Dimpled mugs are still popular: they are the trade's equivalent to a reproduction Georgian window, except that the original never existed.

Measurement

Beer can be served only in measured amounts of one-third-pint, half-pint (10 oz), and multiples of half-a-pint. It is therefore illegal to sell two-thirds of a pint. Stamped glasses are unavoidable, even if you have beer meters.

The DTI National Weights and Measures Laboratory licenses local authorities to stamp glasses. Almost all pub glassware comes from either St Helens (Pilkington) or Chesterfield (Dema), and are stamped by the local authority at source, as are measuring chambers on dispensers.

Licensees have a legal duty to fill glasses with the requested amount of beer. Legally a brim measure pint (20 oz) glass can hold exactly one pint or up to 1.2 oz more than a pint. Glasses are made with a tolerance of between 0.3 and 0.9 oz oversize. With a pint-to-line glass, the tolerance is bilateral and may be anything from 19.4 oz to 20.6 oz.

The chances are, then, that filling a brim measure glass right to the top would probably give 0.6 oz (10 ml) more than a pint. Filling a lined glass exactly to the line would probably give exactly one pint.

When filling glasses with beer, the problem is froth. Froth is a mixture of gas and beer. The Guidance Notes issued by the Brewers and Licensed Retailers Association recommend that a brim measure glass should contain 95% (19 oz) of a pint when the head has collapsed. With lined glasses, the liquid should reach the line when the head has collapsed.

The courts have recognised that the amount of froth has to be "an integral part of what is purported to be sold provided it is not excessive or unreasonable in the light of what the customer was to be taken as ordering".

In other words, a customer ordering a 'nitrokeg' ale or stout should expect it to come with the advertised frothy head, accepting that he or she is unlikely to get more than 19 oz of liquid. But real ale drinkers expect a full pint, especially if they ask for it to be drawn 'slack' (no sparkler).

The Guidance Notes say that requests for a top-up should always be met with good grace and *never be refused*.

It is not possible to say precisely how much liquid is contained in the head because the surface area varies with different types of glass. The amount of liquid varies too, between the minimal amount held in the loose bubbles of real ale from gravity dispense and the tight thick head of a nitrokeg stout.

Glass washing

Most pubs have an automatic glass washer. The machine needs to be kept topped-up with salt and rinse agent, as well as detergent, or glasses will have smear marks. Follow daily and weekly cleaning instructions for the machine, and a daily check for blocked jets is a good idea.

If you are not sure if the washer is effective, fill a washed glass with cold water, empty and invert it. If the glass is clean the water will cling in a continuous film; if the water breaks into droplets you have a dirty glass and a problem with the washer.

If the machine breaks down, use a double sink, one containing cleaning solution – never use domestic washing up liquid – the other hot water for rinsing. Mix the solution in the exact quantity stated on the container. Too little will not clean the glasses; too much will waste money and lead to tainting. The environmental health officers prefer glasses to drain on a latticed plastic mat rather than being dried with a cloth.

Glass care

Stacking glasses inside one another forces the rims outward and causes chips and splits. Ravenhead have developed the Stacker Nonik to resist this sort of treatment, but it is far better to eliminate the problem by collecting glasses in a plastic basket. This also saves double handling as the glasses can be put straight into the washer.

Drinking

Many pub users have a strange loyalty to the glass they are lent, and want it refilled rather than replaced. People are getting used to the idea of a clean glass each time, however, and progress is being made slowly.

The best designs of glass for appreciating beer are those which taper in at the top to contain the bouquet (*Tulip, Barmaster*). Beer aroma is best tried when the glass is half full by covering the brim and swirling the beer to release the bouquet. Try the same beer indoors then outside: the difference is surprising.

18 Line Cleaning

Beer is as much a food as bread or meat and should be treated with the same regard to hygiene. Treat the cellar as if it were the kitchen.

Beer lines must be cleaned at least once a week. It saves time and beer if you do the cleaning when casks are changed. Otherwise make it a fixed ritual, at the same time(s) each week, to avoid the temptation to do it when you feel like it.

Ask any brewery technical services person to recommend a cleaning fluid – you want a product that has been tried and tested. Resist offers of 'cheap' cleaning fluids: they can damage equipment and be a false economy. The Control of Substances Hazardous to Health (COSHH) Regulations require you to have a data sheet, which the manufacturers will supply on request. Don't put this off: you can be in big trouble with the Environmental Health Officers without it.

Follow the manufacturer's instructions, which will involve dilution with cold water. There is no point in leaving cleaning fluid in the line for longer than recommended. Nor will strong mixtures do much more than waste your money. And the mixed solution has a short life, so mix it fresh each time you need it.

1. Tell bar staff what you are going to do. Even the most laid back customers do not like a mouthful of cleaning fluid.

2. Disconnect the beer line and immerse the tail in a pail of water. Pull this through to drive out the residual beer.

3. Immerse the tail in the bucket of cleaning solution and pump the solution up to the dispense head.

4. Leave to soak for the recommended time – usually about 10 minutes – then pull fresh solution through. Do this twice.

5. Remove the tail from the bucket and pump the solution out.

6. Immerse the tail in a bucket of clean, cold water and flush the line through very thoroughly. Taste the water to ensure there is no taint.

7. Remove the tail from the bucket and pump the line empty.

8. Connect the tail to the cask.

9. Dispose of the cleaning solution and rinse out the buckets.

Pumps and lines that are temporarily out of use should be left full of water and flushed at intervals to keep them sweet. At intervals of six to twelve months pumps should be inspected for any wear, leakage or build up of deposits.

Sometimes new lines can give the beer a 'pipey', plastic taste, though this does not seem to be the problem it once was. If you find beer picking up such tastes, the answer is to 'pickle' the pipes. Fill them with beer, leave them for a week, then clean them as above.

The last five years have seen a number of companies introduce electronic pipe cleaning aids. These are based upon the discovery that an alternating magnetic field can affect the solubility of some of the salts in hard water. The installation involves fitting a coil around each pipe, close to the cask tap end. These coils are then driven with a low voltage, variable audio frequency signal from a small wall-mounted power unit. The units have some effect, but do not eliminate manual cleaning. At best, they extend the minimum cleaning period from one week to perhaps three or four. Most units are considerably over-priced for their limited utility and cost money to run.

19 Hygiene and Housekeeping

The Food Hygiene Regulations require your cellar to be clean and pest proofed. Mop up all spillage and overflows at once. If beer is left in a puddle on the cellar floor it will develop a skin of grey mould within hours. This is a potent source of airborne spores which may infect the casks. When cleaning the cellar floor and walls, never use a disinfectant, or the pervasive odour will enter the casks and taint the beer. Liquid bleaches or powdered chloride of lime will effectively inhibit mould and bacterial growth. The floor should be scrubbed at weekly intervals and mopped daily. Walls and ceiling should be cleaned down three or four times each year and repainted annually. To avoid paint-tasting beer, leave a halved onion in the cellar whilst painting – it's amazing how much odour it will absorb.

Another source of contamination is the casks themselves. Cleaning of shives and keystones has already been mentioned (Chapter 5), as has casks which arrive looking as if they have been rolled round a farm. Stand them over the drain and rinse them down.

Always stop up an emptied cask immediately with a cork bung, and drive a hard spile right in until it is flush with the shive. There are three practical reasons for this.

- A closed cask stays sweet longer, making it less of a problem to clean and sterilise at the brewery.
- It removes a possible source of bacterial development and infection.
- It is a courtesy to the drayer, who does not appreciate lees running down his shirt-front.

Empties should be removed from stillage at once. Stack them on end, so they can be recognised as empties at a glance. Sorting them into breweries will help the drayer. Most brewers use a code system of coloured bands round the bilge of their casks so they can be easily identified as their property, but there is a lot of duplication. Table 5 may help in the rough sorting of casks by colour code, but the definitive indication is the brewery's name embossed on the front head.

Drayers from big breweries are often reluctant to take away alien casks, even if they delivered them as part of their company's guest beer programme. Try and prevail upon them to take the casks away. Their company's depots operate a clearing house system which returns casks to their owners. Small breweries spend a lot of capital and time trying to recover casks from trade, and it is worth helping them by organising prompt return. In any case, you do not want your cellar or yard cluttered with empties.

20 Air Filtration

A common criticism of traditional beer dispense is that the open spile hole permits contamination from airborne spores. Furthermore, particularly for casks in the bar, incoming air can bring with it odours from tobacco smoke or cooking. These are not serious problems in the normal cellar if it is kept clean and if the beers are being turned over at sufficient rate for the cask sizes in use. The 'bad bar air' argument has an intuitive appeal, but there appears to be no scientific evidence of flavour changes.

However, where these arguments are used as an excuse for not having traditional dispense or for using blanket pressure, the answer is air filtration. After the cask has been vented, the hard spile is replaced with a small metal or plastic spigot. This is connected by flexible tubing to a filter unit, normally wall-mounted. This unit contains a sub-micron filter element, which allows free passage to air but traps any organisms or spores. If an activated charcoal element is also included, most odour molecules will be removed as well. Several casks can be connected to one filter element. Commercial units are available from a number of bar equipment suppliers, but a DIY version is well within the capability of the average handyman. Of course, if they are not cleaned regularly in a bucket of cleaning solution to remove beer and yeast, the cure will be worse than the disease.

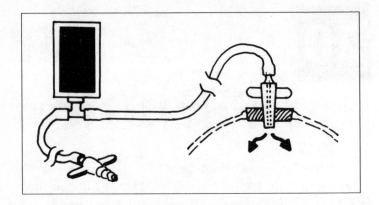

Figure 20: Air filter

Where the 'bad' bar air argument is the main worry, the air supply can be improved by using a length of thin tubing taken to an area of good fresh air, without a filter.

21 Carbon Dioxide

Carbon dioxide (CO_2), a colourless and odourless gas which sets the nostrils tingling, is a by-product of fermentation. It is present in air in small quantities (1% or so) and would be much more plentiful if it were not for the fact that, unlike oxygen and nitrogen, it dissolves readily in water. Thus much of the earth's carbon dioxide is in the oceans.

The ease with which this gas dissolves is vital in producing the refreshing drink we know as beer. The level of carbon dioxide in beer is known as its condition, and controlling this is of prime concern to the cellar manager.

The amount of carbon dioxide dissolved is measured in volumes per volume. At cellar temperature and at atmospheric pressure an ideally conditioned pint of beer will hold just over a pint of carbon dioxide *gas:* about 1.1 volumes. This means that if the water could be removed from a cask of beer, there would be a few pints of liquid left (alcohol, sugars, finings etc.) and the rest of the cask would be full of carbon dioxide at just above atmospheric pressure.

Three things determine the amount of gas dissolved in beer: the temperature of the beer, the pressure of carbon dioxide at its surface, and the time elapsed since either of these conditions have changed. If temperature and carbon dioxide pressure are held stable, the amount of dissolved gas will remain the same.

Temperature is a simple matter, but pressure is more complicated. The pressure that matters is the absolute pressure of the carbon dioxide present. All other gases (such as oxygen or nitrogen) are irrelevant. In a mixture of gases, such as air, the individual gases act independently in producing the total pressure at a surface; each gas produces its own partial pressure. These partial pressures are in proportion to the proportions of the gases in the mixture. Thus the pressure of the atmosphere (1 bar, 1000 millibars, or 14.7 psi) is made up of about 200 millibars from oxygen, about 800 from nitrogen and only 10 or so from carbon dioxide. In all considerations of beer and its condition, only this partial pressure is important.

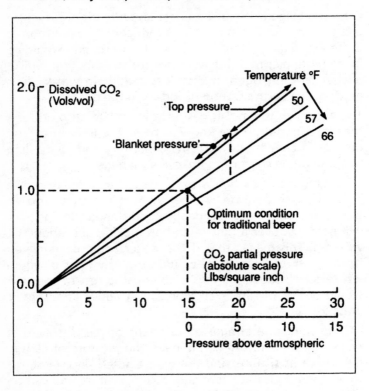

Figure 21: Condition in beer

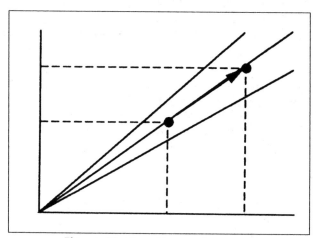

Figure 22: Gas pressure increase

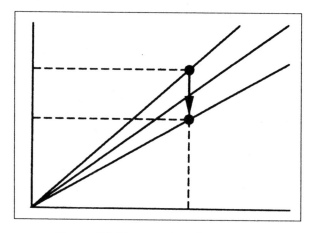

Figure 23: Temperature increase

Figure 21 shows the dissolved volume of gas for various temperatures and carbon dioxide pressures. This diagram allows prediction of the state of beer that has been through any sequence of conditions. For example, if the gas pressure is increased at a constant temperature, the beer will absorb more gas and its condition will move along the inclined line shown in Figure 22. Alternatively, if the beer warms up at a steady pressure, it will give off gas as its condition moves down the line shown in Figure 23.

When a cask of beer arrives in the cellar, the only gas inside the cask is carbon dioxide. The secondary fermentation that the beer has undergone since it was racked into the cask will have produced more carbon dioxide. Some of this will have dissolved and some will be present as gas, pressurised above atmospheric pressure but in balance, as described above.

New balance

Venting the cask instantaneously lets out the excess *undissolved* gas. Then, because the beer is now 'super-saturated', gas comes out of solution over the next few hours until a new balance is obtained. Venting should end when the beer contains 1.1 volumes per volume of gas, the amount for 15° C and a full 1 bar of carbon dioxide partial pressure (i.e. carbon dioxide at full atmospheric pressure, no air having yet been admitted to the cask).

The problems begin when beer starts to be drawn off. Air enters the cask and mixes with the carbon dioxide already present. As the total pressure remains that of the atmosphere, the carbon dioxide partial pressure must drop as its proportion of the gas mixture reduces. The beer in the cask must now give up some of its dissolved gas to reach equilibrium again. As the cask empties, the beer's condition gradually moves down the line shown in Figure 24.

At first sight it might seem that as soon as some beer is drawn off from a full cask, the gas inside the cask will be virtually all air and the dissolved carbon dioxide will fall to nearly zero. However, as soon as air starts to enter and the partial pressure starts to fall, the beer will give off a substantial volume of gas to re-stabilise the situation. It is essential to retain as much of this carbon dioxide as possible within the cask, which is why the cask must be hard spiled at all times when not in service. It takes some time for the beer to give up its gas. If the cask is used up in a day or so, the beer never has time to 'catch up' with the decreasing partial pressure and stays in reasonable condition.

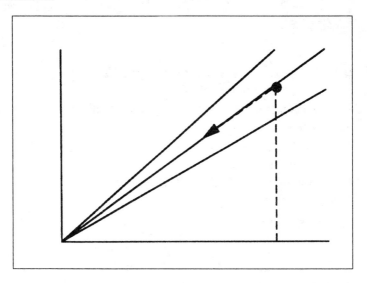

Figure 24: The cellarman's problem

22 Nitrogen

Nitrogen dispense systems are increasingly common. Nitrogen has a number of advantages over CO_2.

- It's much cheaper: you can even make your own!
- It is not easily absorbed by beer.
- It's inactive, whereas a cellar with a leaky CO_2 line can be fatal.

The objective is biological and oxidation control, rather than control of condition.

Nitrogen can be bought by the cylinder, or it can be produced directly from the atmosphere by means of a molecular sieve filter, in which filtered air is pumped through a chamber filled with semi-permeable plastic membranes. These selectively pass the nitrogen content but not the oxygen. Once installed, there is no further expenditure on gas bottles.

Nitrogen can be used in four ways.

- Via a reduction valve (to about 1 bar) for blanket pressure on real ale casks (see Chapter 24). This fills the headspace in the cask, preventing air contacting the beer. Unlike CO_2, it is not absorbed by the beer, nor does it prevent CO_2 coming out of solution if condition increases.
- Mixed with CO_2 (60% CO_2: 40% N) for keg lagers.
- Mixed with CO_2 (30/70) for 'smoothflow' keg beers and stouts. (The CO_2 fraction is given first in a recently adopted convention.)
- To drive gas pumps and ring main cleaning systems: a substantial user of CO_2.

Nitrogenation is the term used for the treatment of keg beer or lager with nitrogen under pressure to force absorbtion of nitrogen gas into solution, typically 25 ppm. The resultant liquid is smooth, less bitter, and has a creamier head with a large number of small but stable bubbles.

23 Other Pressure Systems

CO₂ top pressure

In the 1960s and 1970s real ale was often served using carbon dioxide as the propellant. Pressurised carbon dioxide – often twice atmospheric pressure or more, depending upon the height of the dispense unit above the cellar – pushes the beer from the cask up to a simple on/off tap at the bar. It came into use for cask beers when keg beers (which use the same system) were becoming common. The inert keg beers rely on the top pressure gas to give them condition (often to excess).

The impact on beer quality was disastrous, making cask beer greatly over-conditioned and barely distinguishable from keg.

Customer resistance led to top pressure being supplanted by beer engines. Only licensees who are uninterested in beer quality persist with CO₂.

Keg beers still require a gas propellant for dispense, and CO₂ is used almost exclusively for lagers. Keg beers and stouts use mixed gas (see Chapter 22).

Blanket pressure

Blanket pressure is the term used for systems which replace beer drawn off from the cask with carbon dioxide or nitrogen, rather than air. It is *not* a way of dispensing beer.

The rapid deterioration that takes place after a cask is half empty (large surface to volume ratio) leads to the rationale for blanket pressure. The argument is that by excluding air, the 'blanket' will both prevent the beer from going off and preserve condition. Proper choice of cask size and good cellarmanship make it unnecessary. Blanket pressure is an admission of lack of skill and planning.

Low turnover outlets, especially those with erratic trade, may find it convenient to use blanket pressure if they wish to sell cask beer rather than keg. But CO_2 is expensive and permeates the beer, so modern blanket pressure systems use nitrogen (Chapter 22).

Whichever gas is used, it is vital that the correct equipment is employed. Many breweries suggest using an ordinary gas regulating valve, as used for keg dispense, set to a low pressure – a tenth of a bar or so. This is not satisfactory on two counts. First, the normal regulating valve is not reliable when set at the extreme of its range. The blanket gas can be substantially above atmospheric pressure, giving objectionable over-conditioning. Second, connection to such a valve does not allow venting off any excess carbon dioxide produced by the beer in the cask, again resulting in over-condition.

Air pressure

Air pressure dispense is almost exclusive to Scotland, where it is the predominant traditional method.

An electrically-driven compressor keeps a tank filled with air at a pressure of several atmospheres. This pressurised air is used to force the beer up to the counter dispensers. One would expect this to accelerate the detrimental effects of oxidation (as there is a higher concentration of oxygen at the beer's surface) but this is not readily noticeable. What is apparent is a small increase in the condition of the beer, since the carbon dioxide partial pressure has been somewhat increased and none of the residual carbon dioxide is allowed to escape.

24 Various Valves

Demand valve

The demand valve, or cask breather, is a simple device designed to remove the unreliable aspects of the blanket pressure system.

The breather valve is a demand valve; it supplies nitrogen or carbon dioxide gas at exactly atmospheric pressure *on demand*. The volume above the beer is topped up with exactly one volume of gas for each volume of beer drawn off. The controlling signal for a cask breather is the outside atmospheric pressure. There are no adjustments to set and no internal force balances to go out of adjustment. In this respect the design answers the first of the problems with 'normal' blanket pressure. The second problem is dealt with by the inclusion of a secondary relief valve that automatically vents any build-up of excess pressure; it acts like an automatic soft spile.

In erratic and marginal turnover outlets, where a nitrogen or carbon dioxide replacement system may have to be used to enable cask-conditioned beer to be sold rather than keg, this equipment gives a satisfactory result. It is not worth using in normal volume sales, since it involves an unnecessary expenditure on gas and can lead to lack of care in cask size control, with beers being subjected to abnormally long shelf lives.

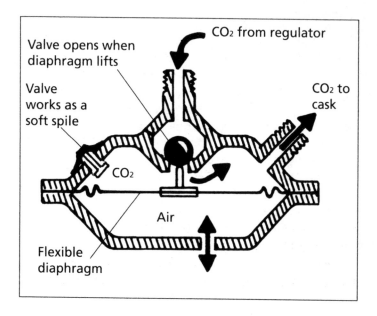

Valve opens when diaphragm lifts

Valve works as a soft spile

CO₂ from regulator

CO₂ to cask

CO_2

Air

Flexible diaphragm

Figure 25: Demand valve (diagrammatic)

One of Britain's major brewers has refused to use cask breathers because they cannot easily be cleaned. This is true, and if beer gets inside the device, it is likely to malfunction.

Check valve

If a cask is stillaged above the level of a beer engine, beer will dribble from the spout. The cylinder and piston valves have no resistance to pressure in the forward direction and will allow beer through. To overcome this problem, a check valve must be fitted to the beer line.

This device is also used where a long or steep pull from cellar to bar is encountered. With beer engines especially, even with efficient valves, the weight of beer in the pipe causes some to run back into the cask before the valve has a chance to close.

Pumps with worn inlet valves, pistons or bores tend, if left unused for a few minutes, to allow beer in the cylinder to drain back into the cask. This causes great frustration, needing many 'pulls' to get each pint. It may also disturb the sediment, giving rise to complaints of cloudy beer.

The check valve is spring loaded, either adjustable or pre-set, and is set so it will not open under the differential head of the beer (that is, the head between the top surface of the beer in the cask and the pump outlet tap). It does open, however, when the pump is pulled, since this produces a suction, increasing the pressure across the valve.

These valves can be fitted anywhere in the beer line between the cask and the engine. Some makes of beer engine can be fitted internally with springs on the cylinder inlet valves to produce the same result. These are known as 'high pressure engines'.

Non-return valves

The non-return valve is a replication of the inlet valve in the pump cylinder. It can be placed anywhere in the beer line, but is best fitted directly at the tap end. The advantage is that beer lines can be disconnected without any beer escaping.

Most pump and cellar fitting manufacturers can supply fittings to suit any size of beer line.

Beer saver

This device, a nylon cylinder, is inserted into the beer line close to the beer engine. At the end of trading sessions a turn of a knurled knob opens a needle valve which releases the airlock in the line and allows the beer to trickle slowly back into the cask. This avoids beer warming in the pipe and consequent pull-off wastage. The *beer saver* cannot be used if the line is less than 3/8 inch bore or if the cask is level with or above the beer engine. If the line has a non-return valve, the manufacturers (Techlink) can provide one which can be temporarily disabled while bleed-down takes place.

Automatic spile

Numerous versions of this device exist, such as the Race Cask Ventilator. It contains two valves: one acts to release build up of CO_2 like an automatic soft spile; the other admits air as beer is drawn off, but in practice a partial vacuum must exist in the cask before the valve will open. The beer therefore becomes flatter than if the cask were left open to the atmosphere.

The auto soft spile mode works well, unless the device is disabled by fob and yeast. But there is no point in restricting displacement air into the cask, so it is better to remove the device when you start serving. As with all such devices, cleaning is not easy.

25 Taps

The many different types of cask tap have three points in common.

- A body with a tapered spigot for piercing the keystone.
- A rotatable valve called a cone, operated by a handle and retained in the body by a washer and nut.
- When the handle is parallel to the cask head, the tap is closed. A quarter turn (90°) of the handle opens the tap fully. A half turn takes it from closed, to open, to closed again.

For connection to bar dispense equipment, a tap with a threaded outlet is required. The three most common types are: straight (single), turndown and double.

The *straight* tap (the cheapest) is not suitable for gravity dispense unless fitted with a turn-down racking adapter. Because it is driven in by its thread end, it is prone to damage.

Some racking adapters retain their fill of beer – until you have moved the glass away, when they promptly discharge their contents on the floor. This can be overcome by angling the adapter.

The *turndown* tap is the most useful for general purposes, for pump or gravity dispense. When used in the cellar it is usual to angle the outlet to give a fair run to the pipe-work.

Double-ended taps allow one cask to feed two dispensers. The open and closed positions seem to be reversed compared to single taps, because the convention is for the open and closed positions to be defined with respect to the cask head. With all taps, the closed position has the handle parallel to the cask head.

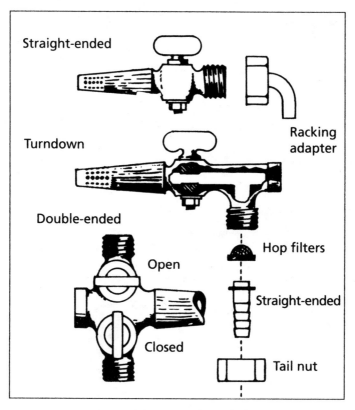

Figure 26: Screw threaded taps

Taps for connection to beer lines have several sizes of thread, some of which are hard to tell apart. This is an historical legacy from the nineteenth century, when individual brewers or geographical groups of brewers developed their dispense systems. The thread sizes are designated by letter codes. The most common are ¾ inch BSP, Y, L, LL, M, S, and R. Of these, Y (Yorkshire) is currently the most common, but a number of large breweries have converted to BSP. These codes are not always marked on the taps, and almost never on the burrs. If acquiring

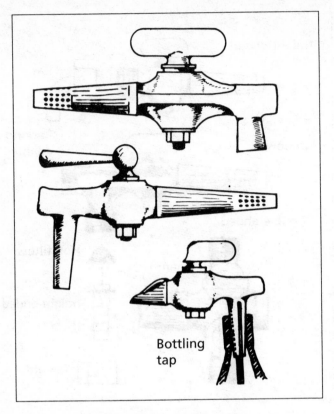

Bottling
tap

Figure 27: Racking taps

second-hand taps, try them first with the beer line tail burrs. Never have a mixture of thread types in the cellar. One exception is that Y and L taps can be mixed providing L burrs are used.

For gravity dispense, the tap is known as a racking tap. The best type has a fairly long tapered outlet, smooth inside, which helps the beer to flow in an unbroken stream. It is also better to have a 'canteen handle' – a long, single-ended handle like a tea urn.

Another long-spouted tap sometimes seen is a bottling tap. This has a very slender, tapering spout which can be inserted well into the neck of a bottle. Narrow grooves up the side of the spout allow displaced air to escape.

Made from...

Traditionally, taps were always made of brass, sometimes chrome-plated. Concern over the deleterious effects of heavy metal ingestion has raised doubts over the use of any brass-ware in beer dispense (brass is an alloy containing a high proportion of lead – a long-term cumulative poison), but there is no legislation against the use of brass taps or other cellar and dispense fittings.

Stainless steel taps seem worth the investment for gravity dispense, where they are operated each time a glass is served, but the plastic cones become brittle and the threaded stud easily snaps off. For connection to lines, where they are operated once each session, plastic is more economical, but they need to be held firmly against the keystone when tapping casks, as they tend to bounce!

Wooden taps should not be used if you can possibly avoid it. About the only use for a wooden tap is for gravity dispense of cider, for the acid in cider attacks brass (not stainless steel or plastic, however). If a wooden tap has to be used, soak it in water for an hour or so before use to let the cork seals 'plymp up'. The inlet holes in the spigot are usually imperfectly drilled, so re-drill them. Be sure the tap it is well driven in, as often the inlet holes barely clear the back of the keystone and only allow a trickle or even become completely blocked.

Maintenance

Taps should be cleaned between use. They can be left soaking in a weak cleansing solution until needed (make sure the tap is in the open position before putting it in to soak). Rinse through with water while turning the handle before using. Taps can also be cleaned effectively in a dish-washer: put them in open, with the spouts down.

Make sure the screwed plug is in position at the spigot end. If it is missing, the tap will almost certainly become blocked.

If a tap drips, first make sure the leak is not from the keystone by wiping around the spigot then feeling for new moisture. Mark the tap so you know it needs attention before it is re-used.

The cone valve that is the basis of the cask tap is an extremely reliable seal. Should the cone leak, dismantle the valve and keep the parts together in sets; the cones bed into the seats with use and are likely to leak if mixed up. Check the cone and seating for a small particle, a scratch or other damage preventing proper seating. Metal taps can be lapped-in using a weak abrasive such as metal polish.

When properly seated and assembled, the cone does not need to be a tight fit onto the seating but should 'float' on the surface tension of the liquid. The nut and washer at the bottom of the valve are there to stop the tap falling to pieces: tightening it does not cure leaks; it merely damages the seating and makes the tap too stiff to operate.

26   **Lines**

As mentioned earlier, the line – or pipe – is connected to the tap using a tail and a burr, but with a new installation the tail has first to be fitted to the line. The line must be of food graded material and suitable for beer.

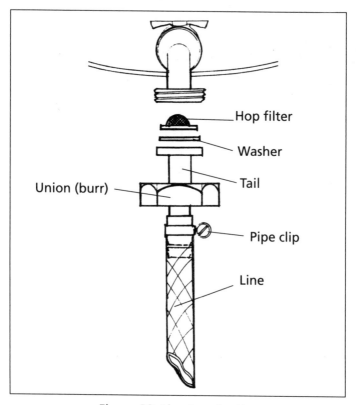

Figure 28: Line terminations

1. You need to know the diameter of the line (³/₈", ¹/₂" or ⁵/₈") and for each end of it have a tail and a hose clip to suit. A screwdriver is needed for tightening the hose clip, but you can get a special clip driver with a cupped blade which makes the job easier.

2. You need a burr with the same thread as the tap or engine.

3. Run the line taking the shortest route, avoiding sources of heat and avoiding sharp turns or kinks.

4. Cut the line to length. The cellar end needs to reach all stillaging positions, but don't have it unnecessarily long. The counter end goes straight onto the engine with no slack.

5. Slide a hose clip onto the line.

6. Slide a burr onto the line.

7. Insert the end of the line into hot water to soften the plastic.

8. Push the spigot of the tail into the pipe.

9. Pull the burr over the tail. Position the hose clip over the spigot fir-tree and tighten the screw.

10. Clean the line as described in Chapter 18.

27 Leaks

Beer leaks are expensive, unhygienic and unnecessary. Some of the commoner problems are described below.

Leaking casks

There is little that can be done if a metal cask has a leak in its structure, but Blu-tak sometimes reduces the flow. Stand it in the best attitude to minimise loss, and inform the brewery at once. They will retrieve it and give full allowance.

If you have to use the beer then rack the cask with the leak as high as possible. Consider vertical extraction if you have the equipment. Vent the cask: less pressure means less leakage. Sell it as soon as you can.

Fortunately, leaks in metal casks are rare. With wooden ones, however, remedial measures can be taken, *with care*, to cure some cases. Leaks are usually the result of careless handling. Letting a full cask drop even a few inches can be enough to give the brewery an expensive repair bill. Many small leaks will seal themselves as the wood, exposed to the escaping beer, swells up. If a cask is delivered and found to be weeping, it should be vented to lower the pressure and left for a few hours to see if it seals. With a leak too large to leave, or one that does not seal, some steps can be taken.

If the leak is between staves – (1) in Figure 29 – examine the iron hoops nearby to see if they can be tightened. Stand the cask on end and *carefully* drive the hoop a little farther onto the curve of the cask. Use a tool with a square end – not a sharp tool like a bolster or a chisel, they will cut into the iron of the hoop.

If the leak is around the edge of the head, then try tightening the chimb hoop (2). Another measure that can be effective is to caulk the offending area (3) with hemp or even brown paper.

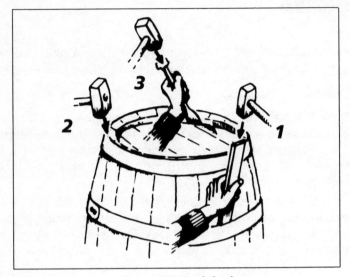

Figure 29: Cask leaks

A leak between the head boards, or from a stave cracked across, is only repairable by a cooper.

Where there is damage to the bung hole or tap hole, and a new shive or keystone will not seal it, then using a piece of *clean, washed* hessian sacking as a gasket will usually work.

Figure 30: Damaged shive hole

Whether you can bodge up a leak or have to live with it, mark it clearly with a thick marker pen and point it out to the drayer. Drayers usually carry "Damaged" labels which they will attach to the cask.

Beer lines

Connection of beer lines need only be hand-tight to be leak-free. If a leak persists, check:

The washer

Washers can become brittle and crack. Traditionally washers were leather; they are generally now nitrile. Nitrile does not seem to seal as efficiently as leather or rubber. Leather, like the wood used for cask closures, swells when wet, so incipient leaks self-seal.

The hop filter

Sometimes the gauze dome gets 'nipped' by the tap face or a stray strand of gauze gets across the face, preventing a good seal.

The tap face

Minor damage to the tap face can be taken out by rubbing with fine emery paper stretched across a flat surface.

The thread types

Sometimes a burr will go on a few turns and feel tight only because the threads are incompatible and have jammed.

Leaks in hand-pumps

A badly-seating bottom (inlet) valve will allow beer to drop back from the cylinder into the cask, sometimes rousing sediment. Remove the bottom of the cylinder and clean the seating faces. Metal valves can be re-lapped with a light abrasive such as metal polish. But don't expect the pump to work miracles: if it is pulling from a long and high-rising line, fit a non-return valve.

If the pump does not deliver its designed half- or quarter-pint at each stroke of the pump, the piston or the piston valve may not be sealing well. If the adjustable stops cannot be set such that the beer engine delivers its full measure for a complete stroke, dismantle the cylinder assembly and check the piston valve. A leaking piston usually requires a replacement piston O-ring (see Appendix 4).

On older types of pump the piston rod sealing gland often develops a leak, but the wear can be taken up and the gland resealed by simply tightening the gland nut slightly: one turn or so is usually enough.

Air leaks

'One-way' leaks on hand or electrically pumped systems are common. Beer does not visibly leak out, but under the pump's suction, air leaks in. The result is persistent fobbing. Electric pumps are particularly sensitive to air leaks, which can sometimes be difficult to locate. Have someone operate the pump and examine the beer flowing past connections in the pipe-work closely; a thin line of bubbles will be seen flowing from the source of the leak.

Split or leaking keystones

A few keystones have faults which cause them to split. If you are experiencing a number of split keystones, your mallet technique is too vigorous. Ramming the tap in too far causes the damage.

The easy way to change a keystone is to up-end the cask, lever out the keystone and fit a new one. However, if the cask is needed at once, the keystone can be changed without disturbing the beer. (See Chapter 13.)

28 Re-racking

The solution to providing good beer for an outside function is not to offer keg, but *re-racked* beer. With proper preparations, real ale takes no more effort to provide than keg, repaying the effort by its popularity.

1. Stillage the beer several feet above floor level. Condition and tap in the normal way, using a threaded tap. Try to keep condition high.

2. Take a newly-emptied cask and remove the keystone and shive.

3. Empty the lees and swill the cask out thoroughly with cold water to remove the residual yeast and hops. It is not essential to make the cask sterile but you must use one that has just been emptied and has contained no sour beer. Make sure it smells fresh.

4. Drain the water and fit a new keystone.

5. Check the beer in the full cask. Connect a short length of beer line to the tap. Insert this line into the empty cask *right to the bottom* and fill the cask from below the beer surface. This preserves the condition and minimises aeration.

6. Keep a close watch on the beer flowing through the line to see that it remains clear; stop racking at the first sign of a thread of sediment being drawn off. The cask of racked beer should, if at all possible, be filled completely, for instance by racking into an empty firkin from a full kilderkin.

7. Fit a new shive.

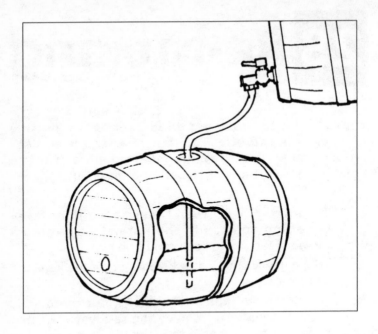

Figure 31: Re-racking

Do not tap or spile the cask until the moment it is needed for service. Bear in mind that the beer is now bright, so there is no longer any need to avoid moving the cask – it can be tipped up to the last drop! However, it will not maintain its condition for long; re-racked beer should be used within twenty-four hours.

29 Fining and Re-fining

Finings work by a process partly physical and partly electro-chemical. The principal action is electro-static, attracting reverse-charged particles into clumps which fall to the bottom of the cask. Cask or 'white' finings are also called secondary finings because there is a primary fining stage during the boil. Primary or auxiliary finings are usually made from alginate and have an opposite charge to secondary finings.

The cask fining process commences with the finings in suspension and the cask at rest. The steps can be viewed while carrying out the three-glass test below.

- Initial flocculation into very loose, fluffy lumps, distributed throughout the beer.
- Accumulation of these into bands alternating with clear beer.
- Movement of these bands to the top and bottom of the beer (the top break and the bottom break).

Over a generation ago, fining casks in the pub cellar was normal practice. Later, local brewery depots took over this task. Today, even this is becoming rare. Finings are generally added to the casks in the brewery as the beer is racked.

But occasions still arise when it may be necessary to fine or re-fine a cask on site. Sometimes a cask gets missed or the fining station injects an inadequate amount. A cask that has had a series of interruptions in its journey to your cellar may need re-fining, since finings will only work efficiently three or four times: 'tired finings'. The first 'drop' is highly efficient and the beer appears 'polished'. Subsequent drops will leave progressively more material in suspension. Finings also work best in beer with a rising temperature: the usual scenario of course is the opposite, with a warm cask on a downward temperature gradient towards cellar temperature.

A cask which has been vented and left to settle for a few days, but is not working vigorously, and is still uniformly turbid when sampled, is unlikely to clear without treatment. If it is an infection, smell and taste should make this obvious. Re-fining will do nothing for bad beer. Should the sample show lumpy or fluffy clumps of sediment in a more or less clear liquid, then the chances are that the cask will clear eventually. It can, however, be quicker to add fresh finings.

Use the three-glass test first to see whether finings will work, otherwise you will waste hours. The three-glass test will show within a few minutes if you can cure the problem.

1.   Get some fresh finings. Most pub chains have one pub in each area which keeps an emergency supply. If not kept at cellar temperature, they change from the consistency of wallpaper paste to that of water and are useless. Ask what the dose is: it is usually 4 pints per barrel, but there are concentrated versions available. Make sure they mean barrel and not kilderkin.

     The quantity of finings to use is both proportional to the cask size and determined by the type of beer - more for the higher gravities. For most ordinary beers a fining rate of one pint per nine gallons should be adequate, rising to one and a half pints for a strong ale.

2.   Get some auxiliary finings. There are a number of proprietary tablets, powders and liquids that assist the action of finings. These are known variously as finings accelerators, adjuncts or auxiliary finings.

Their chief actions are to speed up initial fining and to 'revive' tired finings. There are many brands. Always consult the maker's instructions for their use. These have an opposite charge to primary finings and may work if charges have become neutralised.

3. Fill three small clear glasses with the problem beer. Mark the glasses PRIMARY; AUXILIARY; and BOTH.

4. Add a teaspoonful of primary finings each to the 'primary' and 'both' glasses. Add a teaspoonful of auxiliary finings each to the 'aux' and 'both' glasses. Give them a stir, rinsing the spoon each time.

5. In 10 minutes or so you will see whether one of these treatments is effective. If it is, dose the cask accordingly. If none of them works, don't waste time tampering, get on to the supplier.

One of the most mysterious and irritating aspects is the phenomenon of banding or layering. On occasions, a cask of beer will be perfectly bright for the first few gallons and then suddenly cloudy beer will start to appear, without any disturbance to the cask. This can last sometimes for just two or three pints and then clear beer resumes. The explanation is in the action of the finings.

On rare occasions, rather than all of the sediment sinking to the bottom or rising to the top, thin horizontal bands or skeins of sediment stabilise at positions throughout the body of the beer. These layers, which can be very thin, only affecting a few pints of beer, do not move if left. The only solution is to 'draw through' them. Fortunately, this is quite uncommon. Another common cause of layering is filtering beer back, which can introduce threads of cloudy beer at various levels.

Having decided on the type of finings and the dose required, the rest is simple. Firstly, take out the shive. A de-shiving tool or shive hammer is best for this but a chisel or large screwdriver will do (be careful not to damage the seating).

1. Draw off enough beer to make room for the required amount of finings.

2. Stir the beer using a clean rod or dipstick inserted through the bunghole and rotated in a conical motion.

3. With the beer still in motion pour in the finings.

4. Stir again to mix the finings thoroughly with the beer. Better still, fit a new shive and roll the cask about vigorously.

5. Re-vent the cask immediately with a soft spile.

Finings should be kept in the cellar or a cold store. But don't hoard them: once mixed they have a shelf life of only a few weeks. Some brewers find it more effective to mix finings on the spot in a food processor.

Appendices

There are six appendices which provide invaluable technical information and reference material.

Appendix A1 summarises the supplies and equipment needed, with a description of an ideal cellar.

The need for cleanliness cannot be overstated. The cellar must be kept scrupulously clean at all times. It should be considered a part of the whole beer dispensing system. A cellar should never be allowed to become a storage area for junk or stock like foodstuffs. It is a legal requirement that the cellar is a no smoking area, forbidden to pets and proofed against vermin.

Walls and ceiling should be painted white. A fungicidal paint or emulsion should be used. The floor, which is best made of smooth concrete, industrial quarry tiles or stone slabs, must have good falls to a drainage point. If the cellar is too low to connect directly to the drainage system, a sump with an automatic, float-operated pump is required. The sump should be kept sweet with frequent additions of lime chloride bleach.

Good lighting is important. Fluorescent bulkhead fittings are best as they generate least heat and are waterproof. Ventilation is also essential, but avoid localised draughts. Cellars that are closed rooms need the doors left open from time to time to allow an air change.

A large, deep sink with hot and cold water is needed. The taps should be fitted to the wall well above the sink so that buckets can be filled easily. The cold tap should have a threaded hose connection, or there should be a separate hose tap.

Beer lines should be long enough to reach all of the cask positions without stretching tight, yet not leaving a lot of 'dead' pipe. Each pipe must be marked with a prominent, indestructible label identifying its associated dispense point or the beer type. The lines should be kept up off the floor and should be wiped frequently with a damp cloth. This way the outsides will stay clear longer, making it easier to inspect for inner cleanliness.

A dipstick is an essential cellar tool, but do not take its readings as precise unless it was made specifically for the cask range in question. When casks are manufactured, the brewer will specify the amount oversize the cask needs to be to contain the lees. This can vary from 1 to 5 pints per barrel, though 4½ pints is usual, with other sizes pro rata. Dipsticks can be bought or obtained from a brewery or a cellar supplier.

Some sort of storage system is needed for consumable items and tools. The DIY freak will get great joy out of designing and constructing one. Mason's sell a varnished wood cellar tidy which is wall mounted and will hold your tools as well as essential supplies.

- Hard & soft spiles
- Keystones
- Cork bungs (two sizes, inner and outer keystone diameters)
- Shives
- Tap washers
- Hop filters
- Chocks
- Bleach
- Pipe cleaning fluid
- Hose ('Jubilee') clips

Keystones and shives must be kept dry. If allowed to get damp they will swell out of shape and be useless. These are usually supplied in sealed polythene bags: don't unseal them until you need them.

As well as consumable items there should be a good kit of tools kept in the cellar. Essentials are:

- Wall thermometer. Cheap and accurate electronic remote reading thermometers are now available so the cellar temperature can be shown in the bar, but a max/min will record extremes of temperature which may occur when you are not present.
- Heavy mallets (2).
- Medium and large screwdrivers.
- Pliers.
- Spanners (to fit tap nuts, burrs, keg fittings etc.).
- Pincers or 'Mole' grips.
- Spiling tools (2 minimum, as previously described).
- Dipstick(s) for all cask sizes used.
- Short length (one metre) of beer line with burr and tail (if re-racking is practised).
- Plain straight sided glasses for taking samples.
- Tap cleaning brushes.
- Small scrubbing brush for cleaning shives and keystones.
- Sharp, pointed knife.
- Heavy duty stainless steel bucket(s).
- Mop and bucket for floor cleaning.
- Hand-towels, soap, drying cloths etc. etc.
- Spare burrs and tails.

Table A1 over the page gives some of the more common cellar prerequisites.

A good workman never blames his tools, because he does not attempt a job until the correct tools are available. Get the right gear early in your cellar career: it will give you great satisfaction in being able to do jobs the easy way.

Item	H.Mason Part No.	Item	H.Mason Part No.
Cellar tidy	6/207	Burrs, 3/4" BSP, plastic	
Cask tap, stainless		Hexagon	1/137
steel body*		Round	1/138
Straight	1/100	Wing	1/139
Racking	1/101	Tails, plastic, for above	
Cask taps, all plastic*		3/8 x 3/4" pipe	1/141
Straight	1/102	1/2 x 3/4" pipe	1/142
Double	1/103	5/8 x 3/4" pipe	1/143
Turndown	1/104	Hop filters (packs of 100)	
Washers (packets of 100)		Brewery threads*	1/144
Nitrile, brewery threads*		3/4" BSP	1/145
	1/123	Venting equipment	
Nitrile, 3/4" BSP	1/124	Cask spigot, plastic	2/173
2-way outlet adaptor*		Vent spile with tap & tubing	2/175
	4/194	Plastic tubing (30 m)	
Leather, brewery threads*		3/8 x 1/2"	3/181
	1/125	3/8 x 5/8"	3/182
Leather, 3/4" BSP	1/126	1/2 x 3/4"	3/183
Burrs for brewery threads*		5/8 x 7/8"	3/184
Plastic, hexagon	1/128	Hose clips (10 pack)	
Plastic, round	1/129	1/2 - 3/4"	3/178
Plastic, wing	1/130	5/8 x 7/8"	3/179
Brass. hexagon	1/132	Extractors	
Brass, plain	1/133	Complete	4/192
Chrome plated, hexagon	1/132/CP	Body with bleed tap	4/192/1
Tails, plastic for above *		Blanking plug	4/190/2
3/4" pipe	1/134	Blanking plug washer	4/190/3
1/2" pipe	1/135		
5/8" pipe	1/136		

A1

Item	H.Mason Part No.	Item	H.Mason Part No.
Body pressure ring, white rubber	4/190/4	Dipstick & pipette, vert cask	
Body pressure ring, black acetal	4/190/5	Venting punch	6/220
Body top cap with centre hole	4/190/6	Driver, flex shaft (hose clip)	3/180
Bottom filter, screw-in	4/190/7	Spile easer & keg seal remover	6/221
Tube assembly (without shank)	4/190/8	Cleaning brushes	
Tools		Tap, 13.$\frac{3}{4}$" long	1/109
Spanner CO$_2$ x $\frac{3}{4}$ BSP	6/209	Extractor, 40" long	4/193
Cask wedge (chock)	6/211	Superflex, 10ft long	3/222
Stooper	6/212	Buckets	
Mallet, rubber	6/213	St. steel, 11 litres	5/203
Bung extractor	6/215	St. steel, 6.5 litres	5/204
Dipstick, horiz cask	6/218	Alkethene, 11.5 litres	5/205
Dipstick, vertical cask	6/219	St. steel lid for all sizes	5/206

* State thread when ordering

Table A1: Cellar tools and equipment

Size	Capacity	Weight Aluminium Empty	Aluminium Full	Stainless steel* Empty	Stainless steel* Full	Length	Max. diam.
Firkin	9 gal	21 lb.	111 lb.	25 lb.	115 lb.	20"	16"
	41 L	10 Kg	50 Kg	11 Kg	52 Kg	500 mm	406 mm
11	11 gal	13 lb.	110 lb.	–	–	21"	16"
	50 L	9 Kg	59 Kg	–	–	826 mm	406 mm
Kilderkin	18 gal	32 lb.	212 lb.	46 lb.	226 lb.	25"	20"
	82 L	15 Kg	96 Kg	21 Kg	103 Kg	640 mm	515 mm
22	22 gal	36 lb.	256 lb.	–	–	25"	22"
	100 L	16.5 Kg	116.5 Kg	–	–	984 mm	866 mm
Barrel	36 gal	60 lb.	420 lb.	76 lb.	436 lb.	30"	25"
	164 L	27 Kg	191 Kg	34 Kg	198 Kg	760 mm	625 mm

* Older designs weigh an extra 5lb (2.3 Kg).

Table A2: Cask dimensions and weights

Cross-section	Name	Size	Dema	Ravenhead
	Nonik	10 oz		R710
		11 oz	B761-S1034-0172	
		12 oz		R702
		20 oz		R708
		22 oz	B762-S1058-0148	
		24 oz		R835
	Tulip	10 oz		R736
		11 oz	B003AS1034-0172	R720
		12 oz		R721
		20 oz		R879
		22 oz	B098BS1059-0148	
	Barmaster straight or Crown Viking	10 oz		R1700
		12 oz	B617-S1008-0148	R1701
		20 oz	B609	R1702
		23 oz		R1703
	Stacker Nonik	6B oz		R1886 (stem)
		10 oz		R1770
		10 oz		R1887 (stem)
		12 oz		R1771
		20 oz		R1772
		24 oz		R1773

Cross-section	Name	Size	Dema	Ravenhead
	Rio	10 oz		R1711
		12 oz		R1712
		20 oz		R1714
	Conical	10 oz		R700
		12 oz		R866
		20 oz		
		22 oz		
	Pilsner	10 oz		R 976
		12 oz		R1740
		20 oz	B072-S2110-0148	R 977
		22 oz	B072CS1058-0148	R 978
	Barmaster mug	10 oz		R1186
		20 oz		R1187
	Dimple	10 oz		R404
		12 oz		R796
		20 oz		R405
		24 oz		R797

Table A3: Beer glass identity chart. Product code numbers are for stamped / lined glasses

A3

A4 Equipment manufacturers

Cellar and dispense equipment

Colin Farrar Cellar Services
Howarth Old Hall
Sun Street
Howarth
West Yorkshire BD22 8PT
Tel: 01535 642709
Fax: 01535 647857

Beer engines made and refurbished to any specification, including cabinets and plinths with woodwork to match existing counter-tops.

Harry Mason Ltd
Sun Works
217 Thimblemill Lane
Birmingham B7 5HS
Tel: 0121 328 5900
Fax 0121 327 7257

Solidly traditional beer engines and cellar equipment. Beer engines: counter flush or cabinet enclosed 1-5 pulls. Traditional spouts with roll-over taps, brass with stainless steel inserts. Also taps, extractors, piping, fittings, chocks, buckets, dip sticks, tools, cellar tidies.

IMI Cornelius Ltd
Rawson Spring Way
Riverdale Industrial Estate
Sheffield S6 1PG
Tel: 0114 285 5886
Fax: 0114 232 0067

The Group owns the Cornelius, Coldflow, Dalex and MK brands, as well as the much loved Gaskell & Chambers beer engine company, whose 1-4 pull cabinet beer engines still feature the G&C sling and quadrant motion. Cask taps (here called tapping cocks) in $3/4$" BSP or Y thread in racking (turndown), single and double varieties. Hop filters, washers (seals), burrs (nuts) and tails (tailpipes) in plastic or stainless steel. Beer pumps, Rapidomatic (glass cylinder Metron type) and Cellarmatic (Spheroid) meters and fonts (bar valves). Comprehensive spares list for all components.

Pektron Ltd
Alfreton Road
Derby DE22 4AP
Tel: 01332 832424
Fax 01332 833270

State-of-the-art electronics company who bought the Ormond range of beer engines to complete their portfolio, but these have been discontinued. Taps, plastic vertical extractors, electronic stocktaking equipment, electric pumps & transformers.

Dispense equipment

Angram Design
Unit 11 Becklands Close
Roecliffe
Boroughbridge
N Yorks YO5 9NR
Tel: 01423 324555
Fax 01423 324955

Beer engines of modern design which can be easily dismantled in situ in 5 minutes: clamp-on mounted on 1-3 plinths; compact cabinet enclosed 1-3 pulls; counter mounting. All available with cylinder insulating jackets.

England Worthside TR Products Ltd
Hope Mills
South Street
Keighley BD21 1AG
Tel: 01535 606876
Fax: 01535 610052

Principal supplier to Bass. Clamp-on and 1-4 pull cabinet beer engines. The Paragon cylinder has an acetal body and stainless steel poppet valves, $1/4$, $1/3$ and $1/2$ pint, insulated or fitted with cooling jacket. Responsible for developing the swan neck in association with national brewers. Short

A4

spouts – known here as Signets – are available from £12.50. The variable flow control tap has a short spout with an adjustable knurled needle valve. Bar fonts, check valves, manifolds, electric pumps.

Hi-Gene Beer Pumps Ltd
Lakeside House
Turnoaks Park
Burley Close
Chesterfield S40 2UB
Tel: 01246 273166
Fax: 01246 271486

Beer engines in the following ranges: Ashbourne (through-the counter); Chatsworth (clamp-on, vertical cylinder); Hartington (clamp-on, horizontal cylinder) and Dovedale (1-6 pull cabinets), all fitted with check valves, half or quarter pint cylinders, optional cooling jackets. Extractors, cask taps, connectors, Y unions, air sterilisers and filters. Large range of ceramic, mahogany and light oak hand-pull handles ranging from the plain, cylindrical 'wicket', to the traditional 'truncheon' with hunting scenes. A postal beer engine refurbishment service includes a clean up, replacement of seals, polish of brass and new drip tray for £37.50 plus carriage. Beer engine spouts are here called 'northern' and 'short': the northern being the swan-neck. Short spouts cost £20.

Homark Group Ltd
Pottery Road
Parkstone
Poole
Dorset BH14 8RB
Tel: 01202 734000
Fax: 01202 737526

Believed to be the largest supplier of beer engines. Clip-on beer engines with 75mm width jaws, single and multi-pull. Cylinders (half and quarter pint) are insulated and easily changed. Also check valves, non-return valves and bottle cooling cabinets.

At Homark "swan neck" is the name of a range of free-flow dispense fonts. Beer engine spouts are here called 'northern' and 'southern': the northern being a typical swan-neck, 160mm deep, either $^3/_8$" or $^1/_2$" OD with adjustable sparkler. The southern is more the traditional spout, $^3/_8$" OD with optional tap. Interestingly, none of their sales brochures depicts an engine with a "southern" spout. Short spout assembly costs £17.30.

Microflow UK Ltd
Old Hall Street
Globe Square
Dukinfield SK16 4RF
Tel: 0161 3431557

Supply and repair of dispense equipment to pub owning companies.

Porter Lancastrian Ltd
Nuttall Street
Blackburn BB2 4JA
Tel: 01254 53687

Stanwell Technic Limited
Wharncliffe Works
Station Road
Deepcar
South Yorkshire S30 5SQ
Tel: 0114 2887959

Sole agents for the US-made Flojet 5000-135 gas-powered beer pumps.

Stillaging

Goulbourn Stillage
Winslow
28 Prince Consort drive
Ascot
Berks SL5 8AW
Tel: 01344 21951

Stillages and hoists.

Kayel Engineering Ltd
Elm Grove
Horsham
West Sussex RH13 5HX
Tel: 01403 261026

Auto-tilt stillages and hoists.

The Tilt Company
Marshwood
Bridport
Dorset DT6 5QG
Tel: 01297 678590

Auto-tilt stillages and hoists.

Spiles, keystones & shives

British Bung Manufacturing Co Ltd
Lowland Works
Mirfield WF14 8LY
Tel: 01924 493071
Fax: 01924 480632

Burton Wood Turnery Ltd
Wetmore Road
Burton-upon-Trent
Staffs DE14 1QN
Tel: 01283 563455
Fax: 01283 511526

Also mallets and de-shiving tools.

Eurobung Ltd
Roehead Mill
Far Common Road
Mirfield
West Yorkshire WF14 0DG
Tel: 01924 496671
Fax: 01924 480257

Polypropylene cask closures.

Glasses

The pub glassware industry is only two companies. They do not normally retail to pubs, but a 'phone call to them will reveal their nearest stockist.

The Ravenhead Company Limited
PO Box 48
Nuttall Street
St Helens
Merseyside WA0 3LP
Tel: 01744 452117
Fax: 01744 452185

Demaglass Tableware
Pottery Lane West
Chesterfield
Derbyshire S41 9BN
Tel 01246 274201
Fax 01246 555578

Dema are the main suppliers of glasses with printed logos.

Valves

Techlink Developments Ltd
28 Hatherley Drive
Forest Town
Mansfield
Notts NG19 0PY
Tel: 01623 635228

'Beer Saver' bleed-down valve for beer lines.

A4

Breweries and Beers

Appendix 5 seeks to advise the optimum time that beers should be served. The time is given either from when the cask was delivered, or, more accurately, from a date on the cask, which can be:

BBD = Best Before Date

FD = Fining Date

RD = Racking Date

If the RD is not declared it can sometimes be calculated from the BBD. The latter is usually only there to satisfy food hygiene legislation and can be misleading.

Some breweries give none of this data, but rely either on advising customers directly or ensuring they receive beer ready for sale.

Most brewers use a code system of coloured bands round the bilge of their casks so they can be easily identified as their property, but there is a lot of duplication. A registration and allocation scheme has been set up by BLRA and SIBA, though many brewers still adopt colours without knowing of the controlling body's existence. In the following section these codes are shown thus:

RED   YELLOW   BLACK

Unregistered codes are marked *.

ABC	See Carlsberg-Tetley, Allsopp's, Burton
Aberdeenshire	1-2 weeks from RD.

BROWN   LIGHT GREEN   BROWN*

Adnams   Beers are assumed to be 1 week old on receipt. Older stock goes to direct trade and fresher to indirect. However there is no racking date by which this may be checked. 4-6 days storage is to be recommended for *Mild* and *Bitter*, plus a further week for *Broadside*, with *Old* and *Extra* somewhere in between.

ORANGE *

Ansells	See Carlsberg-Tetley, Allsopp's Burton.
Allied	See Carlsberg-Tetley.

Archers   14 days *(Village)* to 8 weeks *(Porter)*. All beers develop tremendously in the cellar. Bright 48 hours.

YELLOW LIGHT BLUE

Arkell	Vent for 2 hours. Bright 24-48 hours.
Arundel	About 8 hours.

RED   YELLOW   BLACK

Ash Vine   Stillage for 24 hours before venting. Ready 36 hours later.

MID BLUE *

B & T   Bright 1-3 days, but best after 7 days.

DARK GREEN *

Backdyke	2 months from RD.
Badger	*Badger Best Bitter; Hard Tackle:* 24 hours: *Tanglefoot:* 48 hours.

GOLD   GREEN   GOLD

Ballard's   *Up to 4.2% - 24 hours; above 4.3% - 48 hours. Mild* sometimes starts working after 12 hours.

YELLOW YELLOW *

A5

Banks's   3 days. Usually needs 24 hours soft spile. Fit a hard spile hand-tight after this, to be released occasionally until ready for sale. The *mild* is very lively.

YELLOW   BROWN

Bank Top   48 hours.

RED   RED

Barnsley   36 hours.

Bass   **Burton:** *Draught Bass.* Bass should not be drunk young as it goes through an aldehydic phase, later developing into a nutty flavour: 8 days minimum cellar time, but 16 days is recommended. The beer is clean and will keep indefinitely and develop complex flavours. Sediment is 1% - about 2 pints/ barrel. No dry hops. Racking strength is 4.2% abv and 16 days later it should be 4.4%. BBD is 28 days from racking.

ORANGE   ORANGE

Cape Hill: *Mild; Brew XI*: 3 days. BBD is 28 days from racking.

Cardiff: *Worthington Best Bitter, Worthington Dark, Hancock's HB Hancock's IPA:* 7-10 days from racking. BBD is 28 days from racking. Yeast 1-1.5M/ml. Sediment 1-1.25 pints/firkin, which equals cask oversize. Soft spiling not required. *Hancock's IPA* is dry hopped.

Sheffield: *Worthington; Stones; Bass Special Bitter; Cask Toby* (aka *5 Star* or *Blue); 4X Mild*. Vent as soon as possible. Bright 3 days. BBD is 28 days from racking.

Bateman   Allow 6-24 hours before venting. Soft spile required up to 10 hours. Ready when clear. Gyle numbering commences 1 February each year at 001. The number is followed by a code denoting beer quality; which is also shown by a colour code on the cask.

Code	Colour	Quality
DM	BLUE	Dark mild
XB	RED	Bitter
Valiant	GREEN	Valiant
XXXB	YELLOW	Triple X
VA	PURPLE	Victory Ale
SP	ORANGE	Salem Porter

The cask ticket has a six-digit lot number, e.g.:

Week number commencing 5 Dec

↓

4 /49   341

↑   ↑

Last digit of year (1994)   Day of year (7 Dec)

BLACK   ORANGE

Bath 3-5 days. BBD 3 weeks from racking.

Batham 48 hours. bright 24 hours.

Beartown Ready when bright; about 24 hours.

RED   BLACK

Beer Engine 24 hours.

RED *

Belhaven Leave for 2 hours before venting. Clears in 12 hours. Bright 48 hours.

MID BLUE *

Belvoir 2 weeks from RD, but between 1-3 weeks is OK.

ROYAL BLUE   PINK *

Benskin See Carlsberg-Tetley, Allsopp's.

A5

Bentley	See Whitbread Cheltenham
Berkeley	24 hours.
Berrow	24 hours.

YELLOW   BROWN *

Biddy Early	*Stout:* 2 days.
Big Lamp	*Bitter,* 24 hours; *Prince Bishop* and stronger, 48 hours.
Bishops	Twenty four hours; stronger beer 48 hours.

GREEN

| **Blackawton** | 24 hours, but 3-7 days recommended. |

GOLD *

Black Bull	24-36 hours. Matured in cask at brewery for 10-14 days.
Black Horse	2 weeks from RD.
Blackmoor	2-3 weeks from RD. Stillage for 1-7 days before venting. Ready 24 hours later.
Black Sheep	The beers are matured for 2 weeks before delivery. Vent on receipt to release pressure. May need soft spile for 24 hours, after which it should be bright and ready to serve.

BLACK   WHITE

| **Blewitts** | 1-2 weeks. Bright 24 hours. |
| **Blue Anchor** | 10 days. Will keep for 4 weeks unbroached. |

MID blue

| **Boddington** | See Whitbread. |
| **Border** | 7-10 days from RD. BBD is 3-4 weeks from RD. |

MAROON *

| **Borve** | Optimum is near BBD. |
| **Brains** | 48 hours. Soft spiling not required. |

RED   BLACK

CAMRA *Guide to Cellarmanship* 113

| **Brakspear** | 24-36 hours. |
| | WHITE   MID BLUE   WHITE |

Bramcote   Ready when bright, usually 24 hours.

Brandy Cask   7 days from RD.

Branscombe Vale   *Branoc:* 3-4 weeks from racking; BB date is 6 weeks from racking. *Olde Stoker:* 5-6 weeks from racking; BB date is 8 weeks from racking.

LIGHT BLUE *

Brewery on Sea   24 hours. BBD is three and a half weeks from fining, which usually takes place one week after racking.

ORANGE   BLACK   ORANGE
YELLOW   LIGHT BLUE *

Broughton   24 hours.

Brunswick   Casks are not stored in trade and arrival date is calculated by the brewer. Leave for 24 hours then tap and vent. Bright 12 hours.

MAROON   CREAM *

Buffy's   Stillage for 24 hours before broaching after which the beer will be ready.

BROWN   RED   RED ON FRONT QUARTER

Bullmastiff   72 hours. Soft spiling not required, except *Son of a Bitch* which may need 8 hours.

RED *

Bunces   24 hours minimum. Will keep up to 1 month.

RED   RED *

Burntisland   Optimum date is on cask label, but keeping for longer will do no harm.

A5

Burton Bridge Stillage on receipt. Hard spile after 24 hours. Bright in 24 hours but 7 days maturation recommended.

MAROON   GOLD YELLOW *

Burtonwood Vent on receipt. Ready 24-48 hours.

BROWN LIGHT GREEN   BROWN

Burts Takes longer to clear farther from the brewery: allow up to 3 days. Should be sold within 35 days of RD, but will keep up to 7 weeks unbroached.

DARK GREEN *

Bushy's 2 weeks from RD. Needs 24 hours soft spile.

Butcombe 24 hours.

BLACK *

Butterknowle At least 48 hours.

DARK GREEN DARK GREEN*

Butts 24 hours.

Cains Beer should be at least 5 days old and still have 7 days shelf life left (see label). Soft spile immediately for 12 hours. Replace with hard spile and beer is ready after a further 36 hours.

LIGHT GREEN   ORANGE

Caledonian Drops bright 6-8 hours. Bright 24 hours.

Cambrian 36 hours, but optimum in two weeks before BBD.

GOLD   BLUE *

Cameron's Vent immediately. Bright 24 hours.

YELLOW MID BLUE

Cannon (W'boro) 1 week.

WHITE*

Cannon Royall 2-4 weeks before BBD, which is 8 weeks from gyle date. Stronger beers will continue to improve, however.

| Carlsberg-Tetley | **Alloa:** 48 hours. |
| | **Allsopp's, Burton:** 24-48 hours |

GOLD	PURPLE	GOLD
	PURPLE	ORANGE *
		PURPLE *
	PURPLE	ORANGE *

Greenall Whitley: 24-48 hours

		GOLD *
	DARK GREEN	WHITE

Davenport: 24-48 hours

RED	WHITE

Devenish: 24-48 hours

LIGHT GREEN	BLACK

Holt, Plant & Deakin, Wolverhampton: 3 days.

Reindeer: 3 days. Bright 24 hours.

RED	DARK GREEN *

Tetley, Leeds: 3 days

| Cartmel | 1 week from RD. |

YELLOW	GREEN	PURPLE *

| Chalk Hill | 12 hours. |

BLACK	WHITE	BLACK

| Cheriton | 8 hours. Will keep for 4 weeks unbroached. |

YELLOW	BROWN *

| Chiltern | Soft spile not usually required. Bright 3-5 days. Vent 24 hours before serving. |

RED	DARK GREEN

Church End	Leave for 24 hours before venting. Ready 48 hours later.
Clark's, HB	4-7 days.
Coach House	3-4 days needed to develop the dry hops.

GREEN	YELLOW	GREEN *

A5

Cobden's	24 to 48 hours.		
		WHITE	RED	WHITE *

Cobden's	24 to 48 hours.
	WHITE RED WHITE *
Commercial	Lower gravity beers optimum after 10 days; *Old Toss* up to 4 weeks.
Concertina	4-5 days.
	PURPLE *
Coniston	48 hours. Soft spile for 24 hours.
Cotleigh	24 hours.
	BROWN *
	BROWN YELLOW BROWN
Cottage	1 week.
	CREAM BROWN GREEN *
Courage	Bristol; John Smith Tadcaster; Webster, Halifax: 24-48 hours. All beers have a 28 day shelf life from racking, of which about 14 days should remain upon delivery.
Cropton	2-3 days.
Crouch Vale	7 days. Stronger beers will benefit from longer.
	RED BROWN
Crown Buckley	48 hours. Soft spiling not required.
	YELLOW BLACK
Cuckmere Haven	Dry hopped and lively (Harvey's yeast). Stillage for 24 hours before venting. Bright in a further 36 hours. *Saxon King Stout* is a *Guinness/Murphy's* cross and designed for swan-neck and tight sparkler dispense.
	DARK GREEN DARK GREEN *
Daleside	7 days. Drinkable in 48 hours.
Dark Horse	1-2 weeks from RD, but no problems up to 4 weeks
	YELLOW BLACK *

Darwin   24 hours.

RED   WHITE   BLACK *

Dent   3 days.

GOLD   GREEN   GOLD

Donnington   2 days. Bright 24 hours.

Durham   3-4 days from FD. Will keep 3-4 weeks.

CREAM   YELLOW   BLUE *

Dyffryn Clwyd   2-3 weeks from RD.

Earl Soham   Ready when bright: firkins 24 hours; kils a little longer.

BROWN *

Easingwold   2 days.

Eastwood's   8-12 hours

Eccleshall   *Bitter* 12-18 hours; *Premium* 48 hours.

BLACK   WHITE *

Elgood's   7-10 days. Stillage as soon as possible with slight backward tilt.

Enville   3 days. Beers are bulk conditioned for 3 days, racked, dry hopped and stored for a further 3 days in brewery.

YELLOW *

Everards   3 days.

BLACK *

Evesham   Drops bright in 4 hours. Can be kept up to 4 weeks.

DARK GREEN *

Exe Valley   2 days.

RED   GREEN *

Exmoor   7 days from RD, but will benefit from longer.

ORANGE *

Federation   24 hours.

YELLOW *

YELLOW   BLACK   GREEN

Featherstone   12 hours but best at one week. BBD is 6 weeks from racking.

Felinfoel   10 days from RD. Soft spiling not required.

LIGHT BLUE   BLACK

Finns   See Jellystone.

Flagship   14 days before BBD.

GREEN   YELLOW   GREEN *

Foxley   24-48 hours.

MAROON   WHITE   LIGHT GREEN

Franklin's   1 week. Minimum 3 days.

Freedom   *Lager* is filtered and can be served immediately.

Freeminer   24 hours.

GREEN   BLACK   BROWN

Frog Island   3-5 days to let dry hops develop.

DARK GREEN   BROWN *

Fulbeck   24 hours.

BROWN   CREAM   GREEN *

Fuller's   3 days. Bright in 8 hours, though ESB takes longer.

YELLOW   ORANGE

Gale's   Vent a few hours after stillaging, then soft spile for 24 hours.

GREEN   RED   GREEN

Gibbs Mew   *Below 5% abv:* 14 days from RD. *Above 5% abv:* 20 days from RD. Casks are fined at depots and carry the FD on a supermarket price type label.

YELLOW   BLACK   YELLOW

Glentworth	2 weeks from RD.
	PURPLE YELLOW *
Goacher's	1 week. Drinkable in 24-48 hours.
Goddard's	3-6 hours. Good reputation for stable beers and lengthy in-house maturation. A gyle of *Fuggle De Dum* brewed in November 1995 won the Beer of the Year award at a festival the following March!
	YELLOW BURGUNDY ORANGE
Goff'	*Jouster:* 1 week from RD. *White Knight:* 2 weeks from RD.
	YELLOW *
Goldfinch	24 hours.
Goose Eye	7 days.
Grainstore	4 days. Bright 24 hours.
Green Jack	3 weeks.
	DARK GREEN *
Greene King	3 days +. Drops in 24-72 hours.
	DARK GREEN ORANGE
Greenwood's	7 days from RD to develop dry hop.
Guernsey	7 days. RD code is a letter for month (A=January) plus date.
	BLUE *
Hadrian	Ready when bright, usually 24 hours.
	LIGHT BLUE ORANGE
Hambleton	24 hours. No advantage in keeping longer than 1 week.
	RED DARK GREEN*
Hampshire	24 hours.
	YELLOW BLACK *
Hanby	3-4 days.
	YELLOW *
Hardington	Stillage 48 hours. Vent for 24 hours.

A5

Hardy	28 days from RD. Drops in 24 hours.

YELLOW   LIGHT GREEN

Hardys & Hanson	Bright 3-5 days. No point in keeping longer than 10 days.
Hart	Optimum days from RD is calculated by dividing o.g. by 2. For example: 4.6% ABV is 46° o.g. Divide by 2 to get 23 days from RD.

BLACK   WHITE

Harveys	7 days. Can develop haze layers in summer.

LIGHT GREEN   LIGHT BLUE

Harviestoun	24 hours.

ORANGE *

Headless	Within a few hours of receipt. The company take their own casks (usually barrels) to brewers for filling with unfined beer, and conditioning is carried out in Headless's cellars. Beers are racked into smaller casks if required and fined before delivery.

LIGHT GREEN   LIGHT BLUE   LIGHT GREEN

Heather	2-3½ weeks from RD. Stillage for 48 hours. Uses *Maclay's* casks.

RED   DARK BLUE   RED

Henstridge	36 hours. Bright in 24 hours.

PURPLE   PURPLE *

Hesket Newmarket	12 hours.
Hexhamshire	7 days.
High Force	24 hours.
Highgate	*Dark; Old*: 3 days.
High Peak	See Lloyds.
Highwood	5-15 days from RD.

GREEN   BROWN   GREEN *

Hilden	24 hours.

A5

Hobsons	10-14 days from RD.		
			GOLD *
Hodge's	24 hours.		
			YELLOW *
Hogs Back	8 days from RD, but ready 4 days from RD.		
		BLACK	PINK *
Holden's	1 week. Bright 24 hours.		
Holt	24-48 hours. Vent after 24 hours. Minimum cask size 22g.		
Hook Norton	7 days.		
		BROWN	ORANGE

Hop Back	24 hours.		
	PURPLE	YELLOW	PURPLE
			PURPLE *

Hoskins *Old Nigel:* 92h; other beers 48 hours. This information is given on the label.

DARK GREEN *

Hoskins & Oldfield 7-10 days.

Hughes, Sarah 4 weeks for full flavour. Bright 48 hours.

Hull 48 hours.

GREEN	BLACK	RED
		RED *

Hydes' Anvil 7-10 days after RD, when the dry hop flavours peak. Vent within 4-6h. Soft spile required for 24-48 hours.

GREEN	ORANGE	GREEN

Iceni 24 hours.

YELLOW	MID BLUE *

Isle of Skye 48 hours.

SKY BLUE	BLACK	SKY BLUE *

Jellystone　　*Finns Stout:* vent within 6-8 hours, soft spile for 24 hours minimum. Tap within 2 days of delivery.

Jennings　　24 hours.

Mɪᴅ ʙʟᴜᴇ *

Jersey　　7 days. Using Guernsey codes.

Bʟᴜᴇ *

Jollyboat　　2 weeks from RD; *Porter* 3 weeks.

Judges　　24 hours.

Rᴇᴅ *

Juwards　　1 week. Bright 24 hours. Will keep for 4 weeks unbroached.

Mɪᴅ ʙʟᴜᴇMɪᴅ ʙʟᴜᴇ *

Kelham Island　　*Up to 42°:* 4-7 days from RD; *Over 42°:* 7-14 days from RD.

Mɪᴅ ʙʟᴜᴇ *

Kemptown　　24 hours.

Rᴇᴅ　　　　Mɪᴅ ʙʟᴜᴇ *

King & Barnes　　Vent within 2h. Ready when bright: *Sussex* 24 hours; stronger qualities 36 hours.

Rᴇᴅ　　　　Lɪɢʜᴛ ʙʟᴜᴇ

King's Head　　*Up to 5%:* 2 weeks from RD; *Over 5%:* 3 weeks from RD. '567272' = gyle 567; racked on 27 Feb. BBD is 5 weeks from RD.

Bʟᴀᴄᴋ *

Kitchen　　5 weeks before BBD, which should equate to one week from delivery. Soft spile for 24 hours, then hand spile for 2-4 days.

Bʟᴜᴇ　　Wʜɪᴛᴇ *
Bʟᴜᴇ　　　　Bʟᴜᴇ　　　　Wʜɪᴛᴇ　　Wʜɪᴛᴇ *

Larkins　　4 days.

Mɪᴅ ʙʟᴜᴇ　　Wʜɪᴛᴇ

Leatherbritches　24 hours. RD and FD on label.

Ledbury	3-4 days. Casks are non-returnable.
Lees	5 days. Bright 48 hours.
Leyland	Usually clears in 3 hours, 2 weeks from RD or 2 weeks before BBD.

BRIGHT BLUE *

| **Lichfield** | 1 week. |
| **Linfit** | 14 days from RD. |

YELLOW *

| **Little Avenham** | Ready when bright: about 24 hours. Beer is bulk conditioned for 2 weeks. Unbroached, will keep for 3 weeks from RD. |

LIGHT BLUE *

YELLOW   DARK GREEN *

| **Lloyds** | 1 week. Bright 24 hours. Beer is brewery conditioned for 1 week. BBD is 2 weeks from fining. |

| **McGuinness** | 12 hours. |

MAROON *

| **Maclay** | Vent after 3-4h. Bright 48 hours. |

RED   DARK BLUE   RED

| **McMullen** | 48 hours. Vent as soon as possible. |

RED (CASK) *

| **Mallard** | 2-3 weeks from RD. |
| **Malton** | 24 hours. |

OLIVE GREEN *

| **Mansfield** | 24-36 hours. |

LIGHT GREEN   WHITE   WHITE *

| **Marches** | 7 days from dispatch date (on label). Clears in 12 hours. |

| **Marston** | Vent within 4h of receipt to release the 'Burton snatch', otherwise the beer will taste over-sulphurous. Soft spile for about |

48 hours, after which the beer can be served, though most prefer *Pedigree* and *Owd Rodger* after at least another week. Beers are cask-matured at the brewery for 4-5 days after racking. BBD is 35 days from racking. Keystones are difficult to tap and can lead to wastage. At least one publican changes the supplied keystone for a polypropylene job before stillaging.

PURPLE *

LIGHT GREEN *

Marston Moor   *Up to 5% abv:* 4 days. *Over 5%:* 10 days. Vent within 24 hours.

Mauldons   24 hours.

RED   RED *

Maypole   14 days from RD.   Bright 12 hours.

Merivales   See Warden.

Mildmay   *3.8%:* 6h; *stronger beers:* 36 hours. Matured for 3 weeks at brewery.

RED *

Mill   24 hours.

RED   RED   BLACK *

Mitchell's   3 days.

RED   BLACK   RED

Mole's   24 hours.

RED *

Moor   20 days from RD.

Moorhouse's   48 hours.

RED   MID BLUE *

Mordue   Clears in 48 hours. Lighter beers best after one week, stronger beers up to 3 weeks.

NAVY BLUE *

Morland   48 hours.

LIGHT GREEN   LIGHT GREEN

Morrells	7 days.	
		LIGHT BLUE WHITE
Moulin	24 hours.	
		ROYAL BLUE WITH WHITE SALTIRES *
Nene Valley	2-3 weeks; *Medusa*, 4-6 weeks.	
Nethergate	*Old Growler*, 3 weeks. Ready 48 hours.	
		MID BLUE *
Newale	14 days from RD, but can improve further. Bright 24 hours. BBD is 6 weeks after racking *up to 4.5%*; 8 weeks after racking *over 4.5%*.	
North Down	24-36 hours.	
Northumberland	1-2 days.	
North Yorkshire	3 days.	
Oakham	48 hours.	
		RED YELLOW LIGHT GREEN
		GRAPHITE *
Oakhill	12-24 hours.	
		DARK GREEN *
Okells	24 hours.	
Old Bear	One week.	
Old Chimneys	2 weeks. Stronger beers 3 weeks.	
		BLACK WHITE *
Old Cottage	7 days after RD (usually 2-3 days after delivery).	
		BLUE BLUE *
Old Forge	When bright after 4-48 hours.	
		GREEN *
Old Luxters	2-3 days. Bright 24 hours.	
		RED *
Old Mill	*Traditional Mild*: 48 hours; *Traditional Bitter*: 72h; *Bullion, Porter*: 4 days +. All	

beers are kept 3 days in brewery after racking. A further 3 days in trade is assumed before delivery.

Orkney   4 weeks from RD. Casks travelling farther than Edinburgh are despatched unfined. Should reach cellar 3 weeks from RD.

BLACK *

Otter   24 hours.

RED *

Palmers   24 hours.

Parish   24 hours. Beer is conditioned in tanks for 3 weeks, after which there are 3 weeks left wherein the beer is at optimum.

Passageway   *St Arnold* 6 weeks+; *Redemption* 1 week; *Bitter* 5 days. Bright 3-4 days.

Pembroke   3 days. *Darklin* requires no soft spile; other beers 6 hours.

Phoenix   *Thirsty Moon* (dry hopped), 10 days from RD. Bright 48 hours.

Pilgrim   One week. Bright 3 days.

RED *

Plassey   One week. Bright 3 days.

Poole8-12 hours.

Porter   2 weeks from RD.

Princetown   4 weeks from RD.

RED   RED *

Quay   48 hours.

RED   YELLOW   BLUE

Randalls   7 days minimum to bring out the dry hoppiness.

RCH   3 days from despatch date (on label).

MID BLUE *

Rebellion	24 hours. Use within 14 days of receipt.
	GREY RED *
Reckless	3-4 days. Bright 48 hours. *Rejoice* needs 6-12 hours soft spiling.
	RED PINK GREEN *
Rectory	When bright: 12-24 hours.
	GREEN DARK BLUE *
Reepham	6 days. Bright 24 hours.
	BROWN *
Ridleys	One week. Vent later rather than sooner.
	MID BLUE BLACK
Ringwood	48 hours. Bright 24 hours.
	RED YELLOW *
Rising Sun	7 days.
Riverhead	24 hours.
Robinson's	3 days. 7-14 days from RD. Can be very lively.
	MID BLUE BROWN
Rooster's	10-21 days from RD.
	RED WHITE *
Ross	2 days. Soft spiling not required.
Rother Valley	24 hours.
	RED ORANGE *
Ruddles	One week from racking. BBD is 28 days from racking. Ready in 24 hours.
	YELLOW WHITE
	DARK GREEN MID BLUE
Rudgate	One week, though the *5%+ beers* will continue to improve. Bright 3 days.
	LIGHT BLUE *

A5

Ryburn	24 hours. Will keep for 3 weeks maximum unopened.

RED   BLACK

St Austell	7-14 days. Bright 24 hours. *Mild* can start working after 3-4 hours.
Saint Peter's	3 days.
Salopian	10 days from RD. Bright in 24 hours.
Scanlon's	Leave 72 hours before broaching to allow dry hops to develop. Best 48 hours after venting.

SKY BLUE   BLACK   WHITE

Scott's	4 weeks from RD. Bright 24 hours.

RED   DARK BLUE   RED *

Scottish & Newcastle	48 hours. Vent in 2h or at least on day of delivery. Use within 1 week of venting. BBD is 28 days from racking date.

Edinburgh

YELLOW *

Masham & Newcastle on Tyne

DARK GREEN DARK GREEN

Shardlow	3-4 days. Bright 12 hours. Beers are held in brewery conditioning tanks for 5-7 days.
Sharp's	12-24 hours.

YELLOWMID BLUE *

Shepherd Neame	3 weeks. Bright 8hours, better after 24 hours. Should not require soft spiling.

YELLOW *

Smiles	4-5 weeks from RD. Bright 24 hours.

RED   DARK GREEN *

Smith, Samuel	Use within 1-2 days. 24 hours soft spile recommended but found unnecessary with most (wooden) casks.

YELLOW *

Springhead	12 days from RD: usually this is 3-4 days from delivery. Strong ales are matured at the brewery and are ready when bright.

RED *

Stanway	24 hours.
Steam Packet	*Up to 4%:* 2 weeks from RD; *Over 4%:* 4 weeks from RD.

KHAKI *

Stocks	One week. Bright 2 days.
Summerskills	24 hours.

YELLOW *

Sutton	24 hours. Can lose condition quickly.

GREEN   YELLOW   GREEN *

Swale	When bright: 6-24 hours, but better after 2 days.

PINK   BROWN *

Taylo r	One week. Tap & vent on receipt. No spile for 12 hours, then soft spile for 24 hours. Very lively.

RED   MID BLUE

Teignworthy	48 hours.

DARK GREEN *

Thompson's	4-5h.

RED *

Thwaites	24 hours. Vent as soon as possible.

BROWN   WHITE

Tigertops	Vent ASAP and leave on soft spile to release snatch. Lighter beers 3 days; darker and stronger beers 7-10 days.

GREEN   PRIMROSE *   (ONE BAND ON EACH QUARTER)

Tisbury	Bright 24 hours. Sell within 1 month of RD.
Titanic	7 days.

RED   BLACK   GREY *

A5

Tolly Cobbold	One week. Bright 24 hours.
Tomintoul	*Weaker beers:* 2 weeks from RD. *Stronger beers* will improve up to BBD, which is 4 weeks from racking date.
Tomlinson's	*Up to 4.5%:* 14 days from RD; *Above 4.5%:* 28 days from RD.

RED   YELLOW   RED *

Townes	1-2 weeks. Brewery conditioning is 2 weeks for light beers and 3 weeks for 5%+.
Traquair	*Bear Ale:* 14 days.
Tring	*Lighter beers* 4-6 weeks. *7.0%+ beers* 6 months +. Bright 48 hours.

BLACK   BLUE   YELLOW *

Uley	*Bitter:* 1 week; *Old Spot, Pig's Ear:* 4-12 weeks; *Pigor Mortis, Old Rick:* 4-6 weeks.

LIGHT BLUE *

Ushers	7 days before BBD, which is 28 days from racking. Bright 48 hours.

ORANGE   WHITE

DARK GREEN   BROWN

Vale	24 hours. Use within 3 weeks of FD.

RED YELLOW *

Vaux	24-48 hours. Vent in 1 hour.

RED   YELLOW

Viking	4 days. Leave for 24 hours before broaching.
Wadworth	5 days (7 days from racking). Beer is racked with a low yeast count.

LIGHT BLUE   BROWN

DARK GREEN LIGHT BLUE

Ward 's	*Thorne Best Bitter* (dry hopped) 1 week. Minimum 2 days.

DARK GREEN   BLACK

Warden	24 hours.
	DARK GREEN *
Warwickshire	3 weeks from RD.
Watkin	Settles in 6 hours. BBD is 4 weeks from racking date.
Weetwood	3 days.
Wells	24 hours.
	MID BLUE LIGHT BLUE
Welsh Brewers	See Bass (Cardiff).
West Berkshire	2-3 days from receipt. Should be about 5 days from FD.
	BLUE ORANGE BLUE
Whim	24 hours.
	DARK GREEN DARK GREEN *
Whitbread	**Manchester:** *Boddington:* 12-24 hours, 7 days from racking.
	BLACK YELLOW BLACK*
	Castle Eden & Cheltenham: 10 gallon casks ready 4-6 hours; 18 gallon, 8-10 hours. Better after 24 hours.
	MID BLUE MID BLUE
Whitby's	1 month from RD. Beers are brewery-matured for 1 week.
White	4 weeks from RD.
	RED WHITE BLUE
Wickwar	48 hours. Bright 24 hours.
	LIME GREEN RED LIME GREEN
Wild's	10 days. Ready 24-48 hours.
	RED BLACK *
Willy's	7 days for dry hop to develop.
	GREEN BLUE GREEN
Wolf	2 weeks from RD.

A5

Wood   3-4 weeks from RD.

                                              RED   BLACK *

Woodforde's   One week. Ready 48 hours.

                                           YELLOW   YELLOW

                                                        BLACK *

Worldham   24 hours.

                                            WHITE   WHITE

                          WHITE   BROWN   WHITE *

                          WHITE   YELLOW   WHITE *

Wychwood   2-3 days.

                                                        RED *

Wye Valley   4 days.

Wyre Piddle   2-3 weeks from RD.

                                                      WHITE *

Yates   24 hours.

York   48 hours.

                    BURGUNDY   WHITE   BURGUNDY *

Young's   Ready when bright, usually 24 hours.

                                      LIGHT GREEN   BROWN

                    BROWN   YELLOW   LIGHT GREEN

Fault Finder

This Appendix lists some problems that can arise with traditional beer and gives suggestions for causes to investigate.

Appearance

Cloudy beer	**From connecting new cask**	Beer is still working, not yet dropped bright.
		Cask is infected (taste/smell will indicate).
		Beer has been disturbed in the cask – spile released too quickly, cask knocked, beer disturbed by filtering back.
		Sediment in lines from previous cask.
	Suddenly during dispense	End of the cask.
		Cask has been moved or disturbed.
		Finings have 'layered'.
	Continually	Dirty beer lines or pumps.
		Leaky pumps 'running back'.
		Habitually filtering back poor beer.
		If frequent with finishing casks, over tilting of the cask.
Hazy beer		Lesser versions of the causes above.
		Beer has been allowed to get too cold.
Lumps and 'floaters' in beer		Dirty pipes and pumps.
		Hop filter missing or damaged.

A6

Taste

Flat   Over venting, inadequate use of hard spile.
                         Beer has been, or is, too warm.
                         Poor glass washing.
                         Beer too long in stock.
                         Beer ruined by filtering back poor beer.

Gassy   Insufficient venting.
                         Beer has been conditioned at too low a
                         temperature.

Fruity/estery   Feature of the brewer's yeast – not your fault.
(banana,   Too old – esters have reduced to fuse alcohols
strawberry,   and acids.
apple or
pear)

Harsh,   Beer is 'green', not long enough in cask to
rough   condition.
palate

Sour, acetic   Infected, beer too long on dispense.
                         Infected, filtering back old beer.
                         Infected, beer too long in stock.

Warm,   Too old – ethanol converting into higher,
prickly   solvent-like alcohols.

Dispense

Fobbing on dispense
Air leak somewhere in the dispense system (may not show up as a beer leak, can be just 'one-way').

Dirty pipes.

Beer line has become kinked.

Pump will not pull full measure
Adjustable stop not set correctly for full stroke. If adjustment does not help, then:

Leaky valve at pump cylinder inlet, leaking valve in piston or wear in pump barrel.

Pump handle springs back
Cask tap not fully turned on.

Cask still spiled.

Beer pipe kinked.

Pump handle will not return
Piston valve is blocked or jammed (common if pumps are left out of use for a long period).

Pump dribbles after use
Beer too lively, still working and releasing gas in the beer lines and pump barrel.

Some parts of the beer lines run above the level of pump outlet.

Cellar

Keystones frequently split
The tap is not being held square to the keystone and in the centre of the cut-out.

Excessive force with the mallet.

A6

Glossary

Acetaldehyde	Ethenal. CH_3CHO, formed by oxidation of *ethanol*. Tastes fruity, mainly apple.
Alcohols	A class of organic compounds derived from the hydrocarbons, one or more hydrogen atoms in molecules of the latter being replaced by hydroxyl groups. Only *ethanol* is desirable in alcoholic drinks. Higher alcohols such as methanol (wood alcohol) are poisonous and produce terrible hangovers.
Auto-Bak	See *economiser*.
Autovac	See *economiser*.
Barrel	36 gallon nominal cask.
Belly	See *bilge*.
BSP	British Standard Pipe thread. 3/4" BSP is the modern standard for beer lines.
Beer engine	Hand-operated suction pump, usually counter mounted, for pumping beer from the cellar to the bar. Also known as hand-pump[ed] or hand pull[ed] beer engine.
Bilge	Centre (belly) of cask – the widest diameter
Bung	The hole in the *head* of a cask, diametrically opposite the *shive*. Contains the *keystone*.
Burr	A union, or cupped nut, which holds the two parts of a pipe joint together. It is put over the tail before the latter is fitted

to the pipe, and has a washer and sometimes a hop filter inserted before connection.

Bush	Brass insert in wooden casks to receive the *keystone* or *shive.*
Cant	The short D-shaped planks in the *head* of a wooden cask
Centres	The longest planks in the *head* of a wooden cask.
Chimb	The projecting rim at each end of a cask, on wooden casks where the *staves* overlap the *heads.* Pronounced "chime".
Cone	The moving part of a cask tap, operated by the handle.
Economiser	The generic term for what is usually called Autovac, a corruption of the proprietory Auto-Bak: a pipe connecting a beer engine drip-tray to the top of the pump.
Ethanol	Ethyl alcohol, or spirits of wine. C_2H_5OH. The active content of alcoholic drinks. Colourless and odourless, but creates a warming sensation in the throat and chest.
Fir tree	The grooved part of the *spigot* of a *tail,* designed to grip the inside of the pipe.
Firkin	9 gallon cask. From Middle Dutch vierdekijn = fourth part [of a barrel].
Handpull	The operating handle of a beer engine.
Handpump	See *beer engine.*
Head	Cask end. The front head holds the *keystone.*
Headspace	The space between the surface of a liquid and the top of its container.
Hogshead	54 gallon cask. Historically a London beer hogshead was 54 gallons and an ale

A7

	hogshead was 48; elsewhere all were 51 gallons.
Hoop	Iron retaining band around wooden cask.
Keystone	Wooden or nylon closure for the bung-hole of a cask. A central section can be punched through by the *spigot* of a tap.
Kilderkin	18 gallon cask. The Middle English term probably came from the Middle Dutch kinderkin = small kintal; kintal being a weight of 100 lbs or 1 cwt. But 180 lbs of beer is no small hundredweight.
Lees	Dregs. Unusable material left in cask after beer has been dispensed. Contains spent hops, yeast and finings. A cask should be sufficiently oversized to contain its lees without detracting from the nominal capacity.
Mug	Usually a half or one pint glass with a handle.
Pin	Four and a half gallon cask.
Pitch	See *bilge*.
Pot	Half or one pint glass with a handle.
Python	Insulated tube through which beer lines are run, usually surrounding a refrigeration pipe. There should be separate pythons for real ale as the temperature is usually set for lagers and will be too cold for draught beers.
Quality	Brewery staff refer to their wares as qualities, e.g. mild, bitter, best bitter.
Quarter	Area of a cask's side between the *chimb* and the *bilge*.
Shive	Wooden or nylon closure bung for belly-hole of a cask. A reduced central section (tut) can be punched through to fit a

	spile and admit air so the beer can flow from the tap. Middle Dutch shieve = disc.
Sleever	A plain, conic section glass with no handle.
Spigot	The tapered end of a cask tap or *tail*.
Spile	Peg made from close-grained timber (hard), or open-grained timber (soft), inserted in the shive to control the carbon dioxide content of the beer. Middle Dutch = wooden peg.
Stave	Curved wooden planks forming the body of a cask. The *shive stave* is wider than the rest to accommodate the *bung* hole.
Strig	The stalk of a leaf or hop cone.
Tail	A pipe connector, comprising a spigot which is retained in the pipe by a hose clip. The face which mates with the tap is held in position by a *burr*, which must be placed over the pipe before the tail is inserted.
Tut	The disk at the centre of a *shive* which is punched through when venting. The only mention of this sense of the word in O.E.D. is a base in rounders, which has the dialect name of 'tut-ball'.
Ullage	Beer which should be there but isn't, usually either because the cask was underfilled, or because sufficient allowance was not made for lees. Originally the word meant the quantity required to make good the loss by leakage or absorption. Modern usage equates ullage to *lees*.

JOIN CAMRA

If you like good beer and good pubs you could be helping the fight to preserve, protect and promote them. CAMRA was set up in the early seventies to fight against the mass destruction of a part of Britain's heritage.

The giant brewers are still pushing through takeovers, mergers and closures of their smaller regional rivals. They are still trying to impose national brands of beer and lager on their customers whether they like it or not, and they are still closing down town and village pubs or converting them into grotesque 'theme' pubs.

CAMRA wants to see genuine free competition in the brewing industry, fair prices, and, above all, a top quality product brewed by local breweries in accordance with local tastes, and served in pubs that maintain the best features of a tradition that goes back centuries.

As a CAMRA member you will be able to enjoy generous discounts on CAMRA products and receive the highly rated monthly newspaper What's Brewing. You will be given the CAMRA members' handbook and be able to join in local social events and brewery trips.

To join, complete the form below and, if you wish, arrange for direct debit payments by filling in the form overleaf and returning it to CAMRA. To pay by credit card, contact the membership secretary on (01727) 867201.

Full membership £14; Joint (two people at the same address) membership £17; Life membership £168/£204. Student, pensioner, unemployed, disabled £8. Joint pensioners £11.

Please delete as appropriate:

I/We wish to become members of CAMRA.

I/We agree to abide by the memorandum and articles of association of the company.

I/We enclose a cheque/p.o. for £   (payable to CAMRA Ltd.)

Name(s)

Address

Signature(s)

CAMRA Ltd., 230 Hatfield Road, St Albans, Herts AL1 4LW

INSTRUCTIONS TO YOUR BANK TO PAY DIRECT DEBITS

Please complete parts 1 to 4 to instruct your bank to make payments directly from your account.

Return the form to Campaign for Real Ale, 230 Hatfield Road, StAlbans, Herts AL1 4LW.

To the Manager

1 Please write the full postal address of your bank branch in the box above.

2 Name(s) of account holder(s):

Address:

Post Code:

3 Account Number:

Banks may refuse to accept instructions to pay direct debits from some types of account.

Direct debit instructions should only be addressed to banks in the United Kingdom.

| 9 | 2 | 6 | 1 | 2 | 9 |

CAMRA Computer Membership No. (for office use only)

Originator's Identification No.

4 Your instructions to the bank, and signature.

• I instruct you to pay direct debits from my account at the request of Campaign for Real Ale Limited.

• The amounts are variable and are to be debited annually.

• I understand that Campaign for Real Ale Limited may change the amount only after giving me prior notice.

• PLEASE CANCEL ALL PREVIOUS STANDING ORDER INSTRUCTIONS IN FAVOUR OF CAMPAIGN FOR REAL ALE LIMITED.

• I will inform the bank in writing if I wish to cancel this instruction.

• I understand that if any direct debit is paid which breaks the terms of this instruction, the bank will make a refund.

Signature(s)   Date

The CAMRA Books range of guides helps you search out the best in beer (and cider) and brew it at home too!

Buying in the UK

All our books are available through bookshops in the UK. If you can't find a book send for a free catalogue to the CAMRA address below. CAMRA members should refer to their regular monthly newspaper *What's Brewing* for the latest details and member special offers. CAMRA books are also available by mail-order (postage free) from: CAMRA Books, 230 Hatfield Road, St Albans, Herts, AL1 4LW. Cheques made payable to CAMRA Ltd. Telephone your credit card order on 01727 867201.

Buying outside the UK

CAMRA books are also sold in many book and beer outlets in the USA and other English-speaking countries. If you have trouble locating a particular book, use the details below to order by mail or fax (+44 1727 867670).

Carriage of £3.00 per book (Europe) and £6.00 per book (US, Australia, New Zealand and other overseas) is charged.

UK Booksellers

Call CAMRA Books for distribution details and book list. CAMRA Books are listed on all major CD-ROM book lists and on our Internet site: http://www.camra.org.uk

Overseas Booksellers

Call or fax CAMRA Books for details of local distributors.

Distributors are required for some English language territories. Rights enquiries (for non-English language editions) should be addressed to the managing editor.

Good Beer Guide to Prague & Czech Republic

by Graham Lees   256 pages   Price: £8.99   ISBN 1-85249-122-1

A glorious guide to Czech brewing history as well as a comprehensive tour around the many breweries and beer outlets with tasting notes, maps, tourist information and language guide to make your stay complete. Covers pubs, beers, accomodation, opening times and food.

Good Beer Guide to Belgium and Holland

by Tim Webb   286 pages   Price: £9.99   ISBN 1-85249-115-9

You'll find details of travel, accommodation, food, beer museums, brewery visits and festivals, as well as guides to the cafés, beer shops and warehouses you can visit. There are maps, tasting notes, beer style guide and a beers index.

Good Beer Guide to Munich and Bavaria

by Graham Lees   206 pages   Price: £8.99   ISBN 1-85249-114-0

The guide tells you where to find the best beers and the many splendid bars, beer halls and gardens, and the food to match. Plus background information on breweries and the Munich Oktoberfest.

Good Beer Guide UK

edited by Jeff Evans – annual publication   546 pages   Price: £10.99

Let CAMRA's Good Beer Guide lead the way to around 5,000 great pubs serving excellent ale – all researched and revised annually by CAMRA.

Guide to Real Cider

by Ted Bruning   256 pages   Price: £7.99   ISBN 1-85249-117-5

This guide helps you find one of Britain's oldest, tastiest and most fascinating drinks. There are pubs and farmhouse producers from all over the country and outlets for Cider's equally drinkable cousin, Perry.

Known Gems & Hidden Treasures
– A Pocket Guide to the Pubs of London

by Peter Haydon   224 pages   Price: £7.99   ISBN 1-85249-118-3

If you visit London, then you need this guide to the well-known and historic pubs you must not miss, and also to the pubs which are hidden gems. Discover pubs with theatrical, sporting and historical connections.

Good Pub Food

by Susan Nowak   448 pages   Price: £9.99   ISBN 1-85249-116-7

Pubs all over the UK serving traditional and exotic cuisine. A great way to discover Britain's 'locals', often run by top chefs.

Room at the Inn

by Jill Adam   242 pages   Price: £8.99   ISBN 1-85249-119-1

Travellers and tourists looking for a traditional British alternative to bland impersonal hotels need look no further than this guide. Contains almost 350 inns which provide Bed and Breakfast as well as excellent real ale.

Guide to Home Brewing

Graham Wheeler   240 pages   Price: £6.99   ISBN 1-85249-112-4

The definitive beginner's guide to home brewing. The principles, equipment and ingredients are explained and many recipes given.

Brew your own Real Ale at Home

by Graham Wheeler and Roger Protz

196 pages   Price: £6.99   ISBN 1-85249-113-2

This book contains recipes which allow you to replicate some famous cask-conditioned beers or to customise brews to your own particular taste.

Brew Classic European Beers at Home

by Graham Wheeler and Roger Protz

196 pages   Price: £8.99   ISBN 1-85249-117-5

Keen home brewers can now recreate some of the world's classic beers: pale ales, milds, porters, stouts, Pilsners, Alt, Kolsch, Trappist, wheat beers, sour beers, even the astonishing fruit lambics of Belgium, and many more.